A
Cowboy
Never Lies
2

Dan Burnett

© Copyright 1998
NEW WEST PRESS
Hamilton, Washington
U.S.A.

Helen
May your saddle
never slip

Dan Burnett

A COWBOY NEVER LIES 2

Copyright © 1999 by Dan Burnett

ISBN: 0-9652375-1-6

Library of Congress Catalog Card Number: 98-067159

Publisher: New West Press, Hamilton, Washington, U.S.A.

Photography: Front Cover Portrait by Annette Medford.
Back Cover — Bull rider Burnett in perfect form.
(Rodeo Photographer Unknown)

Cover Design: BMR Design, Mount Vernon, Washington

Book Design: A2Z Graphics, Sedro-Woolley, Washington

Editor: Diane Freethy

ATTENTION CORPORATIONS AND ORGANIZATIONS!

Quantity discounts are available for bulk purchases
of this book for premiums, fundraisers or gift
giving. For information, contact:

**MARKETING DEPARTMENT
NEW WEST PRESS
PO BOX 32, HAMILTON, WA 98255
360/826-4130**

Printed in the United States of America

TABLE OF CONTENTS

DEDICATION

To my folks.
Thanks for putting up with me.

ACKNOWLEDGEMENTS

*I gratefully acknowledge everyone who helped
to produce this book, and especially . . .*

☆ My good buddy WAYNE GREENOUGH for
   encouraging me to write.
☆ DIANE FREETHY for her laborious work,
   fine editing and expert counsel.
☆ MARK ORTMAN for direction and inspiration.
☆ JACQUE BEAMER for her exceptional cover
   design.
☆ ANNETTE MEDFORD for my cover photo.
☆ BILL SMITH for his indispensable computer
   coaching and maintenance.
☆ My publicists: THE FOWLERS, DEBORAH
   MOSKOWITZ and RACHEL WEINER.

And to all my horseshoeing customers for letting me
test-drive my stories around their kitchen tables.

INTRODUCTION

After my first book was on bookstore shelves for awhile, folks started asking me questions like: Are you still married to Waydene? Did you and Levi ever make another road trip? And, what happened to Orville and Jake?

I'll answer the first question right now. No. Waydene had about all she could take. She loaded up her new washer and dryer and went to looking for one of them responsible types. As for the rest of them . . . well, there's a whole lot more to tell, and that's why I wrote this here book.

In *A Cowboy Never Lies* I told you that cowboys have a way of making a mockery of any sacred event. I told you about how me and Jake darn near ruined his wedding. What I didn't tell you was that me and Jake had a history of causing nuptial disturbances. In the story *Uninvited*, me, Jake and a couple of hounds turn an ordinary wedding into an X-rated circus.

Yep! Me and Levi took many road trips together. Some were memorable and some we'd just as soon forget. But there was one fishing trip I'll never forget. Now, fishing is not a natural part of a cowboy's heritage. Even so, we did possess enough natural instinct to avoid things such as killer whales, electric eels and piracy. But, you'll have to read *Off The Hook* to find out how we managed to escape the lure of a pair of lovesick mountain women.

4

As for Orville, he ain't changed much. Except now he has a feline companion he calls Good Eye. This time I get the upper hand, Good Eye gets the snake and Orville gets a secret message in *Live Wire*.

While Orville may be the simplest cowboy I ever run with, Clyde was the most stubborn. If you don't believe it, just ask his horse. He backs me up on that in *Clyde's Arc*.

One of the best pranks I ever played was on an ole boy name of Cody. In *Look Who's Talking* you'll find out why you should never turn your back on a cowboy.

And speaking of pranks, when it comes to inventing them, ole Hank is the meanest cowboy I know. One thing's for sure, when the two of us get together you'd better run for cover or you'll end up like ole Jumpy does in *Bell of the Ball*.

Some of the characters in my stories are like ingrown toenails. They just keep hanging on. And then there's Virgil. Some boys just can't make a hand no matter how hard they try. It wasn't me, though, that gave him the boot. In *Dressed to Kill* you'll find out why it takes more than a Lone Ranger training video to become a real cowboy.

Being a real cowboy myself, I'm grateful that I had the opportunity to meet a lot of good folks when I was rodeoing. There was the clowns, the announcers, buckle bunnies, fans, and a whole bunch more. But you'll have to read *Port of Entry* to find out why I'm so grateful for stock contractors.

Before you go to thinking I'm always the getter and never the gotten, you ought to read *Room At The Inn*. Clint really gets one over on me this time. Worst of it is, I don't remember what I did to pay him back. But I'll think of it someday, and maybe I'll get a chance to tell you about it in my next book.

By the way, if you have heard me telling some of my other stories on the radio and you've got a favorite you'd like to see in my next book, give my publishers a call and tell them about it. Thanks!

Meanwhile, the best way I know to get started with this book is to saddle up with me and ole Levi as we take a wannabee archeology professor on another cowboy adventure in *Lost Tribe of the Pecos*.

Lost Tribe of the Pecos

Believe it or not, the little town I grew up in — Portales, New Mexico — had a college. Eastern New Mexico University, or "Enema U" as we called it, wasn't hard to get into. It didn't matter how many other schools you'd been kicked out of, just as long as you could afford the tuition. Enema U got a fair share of Yankee students, which always puzzled us cowboys. We thought it was because they raised so much hell on the wrong side of the Mississippi that no decent school back there would let them in.

You're probably thinking that some of us cowboy types might have taken advantage of the folks from the East. Well, that ain't so. As a matter of fact, sometimes we went plum out our way just to help them out — teach them a little about the local culture and all. They was always eager to learn, especially some of them assistant professors that was looking for ways to better themselves.

Back in the fifties when a road crew was digging around in a gravel pit between Portales and Clovis, they uncovered the bones of some of the ugliest dudes I've ever seen. I saw the picture of what they said was "The Clovis Man" in the newspaper. He looked like some of the knuckle draggers that hung out at the Aztec Saloon. They also found the remains of some of the game these old boys had hunted back in the dark ages, and this

7

caused a stampede of archeologists to descend upon our sleepy little town.

One of the archeologists was kind of famous. After he'd been digging awhile, he started teaching at the college, and soon he talked the board into making archeology a required subject for all students. God only knows what poor ole donkey's bones they dug up, but I heard one of the fellers in the Latin class accused them of being grave robbers and went to calling them "Americanus Equinus Assus."

The local ranchers thought the archeologists were plum crazy. They couldn't understand why anyone who wasn't on a chain gang would volunteer to dig in the desert all day in that heat. They claimed they looked like a pack of prairie dogs with all that dirt and dust a-flying. In fact, that's why everyone went to calling them Yankee Prairie Dogs.

One day at the Wagon Wheel Cafe — that's where the locals sat around half the day poking fun at the Yankee Prairie Dogs — I overheard a couple of ole ranchers discussing the possibility of hiring a few of them archeologist fellers.

"If them ole boys are so dead set on rearranging real estate, they can come on out to my place," one of them said to the other. "If they think digging holes is so much fun, I'll give them some post hole diggers and they can build me a fence. Yes, sir! I could make a bunch of them ole boys really happy if alls they want to do is work in that hot sun all day."

Then the other one said: "Every one of them idiots thinks he's going to be famous. To tell you the truth, I don't think everything they found is an archeological discovery. Why, if they was to turn up an old disc blade buried down there, they'd probably shine it up and pretend it was a relic old Clovis Man used in a pagan fertility dance. Besides, they all dress funny."

If you know anything about eastern New Mexico, you know that anybody that goes digging in those sand hills wearing short pants and shirts just ain't wrapped too tight. The wind out there blows so hard, it's just like rubbing sandpaper on your bare skin. After a week or two them diggers got wise and they went to wearing goggles and kneepads. They even wrapped hankies around their mouths. Boy, did they ever look silly!

One day me and Levi was in the Wagon Wheel drinking coffee. I sure did enjoy listening and laughing at the locals carrying on about the Yankee Prairie Dogs, but Levi was more interested in the Portales Tribune that somebody had left on our table. He opened it up to the Intellectual Page so he could get caught up on the comics, and after a minute or two, he started hee-hawing and handed the page to me.

"Look here at ole Beetle Bailey, Hoss."

It didn't look too funny to me, but right beside the comics was a list of stuff going on at the college.

"Forget Beetle Bailey, Levi. Did you see this announcement?"

"Read it to me."

"It says here that Buck Owens has a special engagement at Enema U this weekend."

Levi grabbed the paper again and started reading.

"Shit! Why didn't you read the whole thing, Hoss? It says the tickets sold out in one day."

"Damn! Just our luck. I love ole Buck. I sure would have liked to gone to that concert."

Levi sat there pouting until a red-headed waitress came over with more coffee.

"Either one of you boys want cream or sugar?"

"You must be new here. Everybody knows me and Levi drink her straight."

"Sorry," she said with a smile. "I'm Sissie. And, yes, I'm new around here."

Levi didn't waste a minute. When that ole boy meets a gal, he wants to know everything about her. Before she got our coffee poured he had found out she had moved up from El Paso a week ago, that she was taking evening classes at the college, and working during the day to pay for her tuition. Oh yeah. She was single, too.

"I don't suppose you got any extra tickets to that Buck Owens concert do you?" Levi asked her.

"No. I have to work Saturday night."

Sissie walked away from our table, then turned around and came back.

"You know, I overheard someone say that all the faculty members get complimentary concert tickets. Even the assistant professors. Most of them have never heard of Buck Owens so I doubt if many of them will go to the concert."

"We never see them faculty boys anywhere in town," Levi said. "Guess they don't think much of our hangouts."

"I can tell you where to find them. Under the air-conditioner at the campus snack bar. When those archeologists aren't out digging in the sand, they're in there bragging like little boys about their arrowheads and pottery shards."

"Thanks, Sissie." I winked at her. "We'll probably be seeing you around."

She smiled and carried her coffee pot over to the table next to us.

"Saddle up, pard." I slapped Levi on the arm. "We're going to the campus snack bar."

Sissie was right. The snack bar was full of grown men in short pants and they all had nasty sunburns. We stood just inside the door for a minute to survey the crowd. Everybody was jabbering like magpies except one ole boy sitting all by himself in a corner. He stood out like a sore thumb. This boy was . . . well, I guess you could say he was round. He sorta looked like Tweedle Dee and Tweedle Dum both rolled into one. While everybody else was chattering, he was scarfing down a double chili cheeseburger and his mouth was plum full.

"He's our man, Levi."

"How do you know?" he whispered.

"Because that ole boy would rather eat than dig. He needs our help."

Levi followed me over to the booth. He wasn't exactly sold on my little plan, but he wanted to go to that concert as bad as I did.

"Howdy!" I tipped my hat. "Mind if we join you?"

"No," he gulped. "Not at all. I haven't had much of an opportunity to get acquainted with the local population." He wiped his hand on his napkin and held it out for us to shake. "I'm Phillip Peables. I'm an assistant archeology professor."

"I'm Dan," I smiled, pretending not to see his hand. "But most people call me Hoss. And this here is my buddy, Levi."

Levi shook Phillip's hand.

"Pleased to make your acquaintance," Phillip smiled kind of pleasant like. "Why aren't you two cowboys out punching little doggies today?"

"Oh, we don't punch no dogs," Levi said. "But we kick cats sometimes."

Phillip's eyes bugged out from under his thick wire-framed glasses. "What?"

"Nothing Phillip," Levi chuckled. "It's a joke."

"Oh. Cowboy humor, I suppose."

Levi nodded. "Something like that."

I still wasn't sure how I was going to get the concert tickets, but I figured it'd come to me sooner or later if I could just get Levi to shut up so I could start up a conversation with that feller. When Levi went to explaining the difference between dogs and cats I interrupted him.

"Me and Levi will be heading for the rodeo in Lubbock, next weekend."

I waited for Phillip to say something, but he was too busy chewing on his burger. I looked around the room, trying to think of what to say next.

"Sure are a lot of your shoveling buddies here today."

"Yes, there are," he muttered as he wiped the ketchup off his chin. "Andrew and Robert over there just found some ancient pottery this morning. A lovely clay bowl. Completely intact."

Levi raised an eyebrow. "Is that good?"

"Well, it means they'll be written up in one of the archeology journals. And they'll probably both get full professorships. A find like that can launch a career. A culture is defined by art, you know. The Clovis man appears to be have been quite advanced. It's a preliminary observation, but my hypothesis is that our find here will lead to valuable data linking these Homo Sapiens to modern man. Just yesterday Andrew found a proximal phalanx with metallurgic remnants encircling it."

Levi tried to look interested. "Uh-huh. Just what the hell does met allergic remments mean?"

Phillip pushed his empty burger basket to the edge of the table and pointed to the ring on Levi's finger.

"One of those."

"A ring?"

Phillip nodded.

"Why didn't you just say a ring?"

"Because it wasn't a complete specimen. There were only indeterminate fragments of . . . Never mind."

"You ever found anything like that, Phillip?" I asked.

"Oh, don't I wish." He sighed. "I might have to return to Cleveland and teach at the Junior College the rest of my life. I haven't found so much as a single arrow-head. You boys wouldn't happen to know where I might find some arrowheads, would you?"

That's when the light bulb — I mean the floodlight — went off in my head.

"How about that, Phillip? You and me and Levi really do have something in common after all. We're all looking for treasure. I just wish our kind of treasure was as easy to find as arrowheads."

"You mean there's something easier to find than arrowheads?"

"Shoot, Phillip. Them things are scattered all over this country if you just know where to look. Don't tell anybody else, but me and Levi even know the where-abouts of the lost tribe that still makes them."

Phillip's eyes bugged out again.

"What lost tribe?"

"Yeah. What lost tribe?" Levi wanted to know.

I poked him hard in the ribs.

"You don't mean . . ." whispered Levi.

Phillip leaned forward. "What's that?"

"Shhh!" I said. "This is top secret. See, there's this tribe of Indians that lives not too far from here. They're still wild as weeds. Me and Levi call them the Pecos Tribe because that's where we always see them fishing. On the Pecos River. No one knows about them but us 'cause they live way back in the hills where no one ever goes."

Phillip looked puzzled. "They fish?"

"That's right. These here ole boys just love to fish. They use spears and . . ."

"When can you take me to see them?"

When I heard Phillip say that, I could hear ole Buck Owens singing in my ears. "I got a tiger by the tail." Hell, I could almost see them tickets in my hand.

"They're dangerous, Phillip," I continued in a serious tone of voice. "They drink cactus wine, and legend has it they turn into coyotes on a full moon."

Phillip probably thought he was listening to more of that cowboy humor, but Levi was catching on quick.

"They're so wild and mean, if they see you, they'll kill you."

"That's right. We can't take a chance on that," I said.

"Why not? You guys have seen them."

"That's because me and Levi know the country. We know where to find them and how to sneak up so they don't hear us."

"I can be quiet. I've been trained not to disturb the natural habitat. I once spotted a pileated woodpecker. I sat silently observing it for twenty minutes before it detected me. They're very elusive you know. I was the only one in my Audubon Club to see it."

"No kidding?" Levi kicked me under the table. "You know, Hoss, I think Phillip's smart enough to get a look at them ole Indians without riling them up. What do you think?"

"I hope you'll give me a chance, boys. The mere thought of such a discovery extinguishes any fear I might have. After all, I am a professional you know. If I were to be killed in the line of duty, well so be it."

"Well, geez, Phillip," I slapped him on the back, "Why didn't you say that in the first place? I guess we'll just have to take you along next time we head on up the Pecos."

"Oh this is wonderful! Don't worry, gentlemen. I'll give you credit when I write this up for the journal."

"That's not necessary," I told him. "Just making you famous will be payment enough."

"Isn't there anything I can do for you?"

14

I didn't want to sound too eager, so I paused a minute and scratched my chin.

"Well, now that you mention it, do you have any of those Buck Owens concert tickets?"

"Buck Owens?"

"Yeah. You know. The country western singer that's doing a show at the college this weekend."

"Oh. So that's who he is. Yes. In fact, I have two of them."

"How about swapping? We'll show you the Pecos Tribe and you give us them two concert tickets."

"That's all you want? Concert tickets?"

"Yep. Me and Levi ain't greedy, but we sure do like ole Buck."

"Well, I certainly can arrange that."

Levi got a big ole satisfied grin on his face and I was so proud of myself that I leaned back in the booth and patted my chest.

"So, do you have the tickets with you?" I asked.

"No, they're in my room, in my credenza. But the concert isn't for two days. I'll give them to you when we meet for our excursion. I've got some free time tomorrow. How does that fit in with your schedule?"

That brought me up short. I had intended to get the tickets and never show up on campus again. I figured Phillip would forget us soon enough, and the way me and Levi travel, he sure as heck wouldn't be able to catch up. And even if he did, he wouldn't never find us. After all, he told us himself that he couldn't even find an arrowhead. I wondered if he might have done better if he put a little more effort into digging and didn't spend so much time in the snack bar.

I looked at Levi. He looked back at me and shrugged one shoulder. Phillip wasn't going to let us off the hook and we both knew it. If we really wanted to see

15

ole Buck, we'd just have to figure out a way to play this thing out.

"How about five o'clock?" Phillip prodded. "I don't want to miss them."

"Oh no!" I said. "Seven is plenty early enough. It only takes three hours to get there. We'll meet you in the parking lot of the Wagon Wheel at seven."

"Splendid! Isn't that the eatery where they serve those sixteen-ounce T-bone steaks?"

"Yeah, but we won't have time to eat in the morning," I said. "Better pack a lunch. That's what we're gonna do. Right, Levi?"

Levi grinned. I could read his mind. Our lunch sacks sure as heck wouldn't look anything like Phillip's.

"That's right, Hoss. If we're going back up there where the hoot owls sleep with the chickens, I'm damn sure gonna fix me a big lunch."

While Phillip was stuffing down his apple pie, Levi and I grabbed our hats and headed out the door. We climbed in the pickup and started cruising around town, and every time we looked at each other, we'd start cracking up. I was laughing so hard my ribs hurt. Then it dawned on me. This little adventure was just beginning, and we only had until morning to invent the Pecos Tribe.

"Levi, what are we going to do? We promised Phillip a Pecos Man."

"Hell, we'll just go out there and sit around for awhile, polish off a sixer or two, then we'll tell him he was too noisy and he missed them."

"That'll never work. First of all, he'll want to go back every day until we do see them. Second of all, he's so quiet he can sneak up on a peckerwood bird. Remember?"

We both went to laughing so hard we cried.

"I hope you got a better idea, Hoss," Levi said after he pulled himself together.

Well, it just so happened, I had come up with a plan. I stared hard into his eyes.

"Oh no!" He stared right back at me. "I know what you're thinking, Hoss, and I'm telling you now, I ain't gonna be no Pecos Indian. Forget it!"

"Oh hell, Levi. I wouldn't even think of asking you. You're too damn ugly."

He hit me.

"Well, I guess, that leaves you out, too."

"Be quiet! Can't you see I'm trying to think? There must be somebody that owes me a favor."

About that time we drove past the Wagon Wheel again and I saw Buster getting out of his truck. I swerved fast and pulled into the parking lot.

"What the hell are you doing, Hoss?" Levi yelled as he crashed up against the door.

"There's our man."

"Not Buster. He'll blow it for sure."

"He'll be fine. I can get him to do anything."

"Sure. Like you can get a mule to rope a steer. This ought to be fun."

"Damn Levi, don't you have any faith in me?"

He didn't answer but he followed me as I hurried to catch up to Buster.

I came up behind Buster just as he was walking through the door. When I reached over and goosed him, he jumped and turned around.

"What are you two outlaws doing in here?"

I pulled a chair out for him.

"We stopped to buy you some coffee, Buster."

"I don't trust you two."

"Hey, you guys," Sissie hollered. "Back again aleady?"

"Yeah, we're back," Levi smiled at her. "Back by popular demand."

She rolled her eyes and went to get us some coffee.

17

"Holy cow!" Buster said as he watched Sissie walk back with the coffee pot and a menu. "That's the prettiest gal I ever seen."

Buster loved redheads so I knew it'd be easy to get him to hold still while I told him about our plan. Trouble is, he'd be content to sit there and stare at Sissie all day, and I sure didn't want that.

"Buster, I'm here to do you a favor," I said to him. "But I'll get to that in a minute."

Sissie filled three cups, plunked the menu down in front of Buster and smiled.

"I know those two won't be ordering anything but coffee. What can I get for you, sir?"

Buster grinned real big. "I'll have a hot dog and a bowl of that tomato consummate."

"Tomato consummate?" Sissie asked.

"Tomato consummate," he said a little louder.

Sissie giggled and repeated it one more time like she hadn't heard him. I could tell Buster was getting frustrated. You see, Buster liked to use big words because he thought they would impress the girls. And they might have too, if only he had any idea what they meant.

"That's what they call soup in France, you know."

"Oh!" Sissie pretended to be surprised. "You mean consommé?"

"That's what I just said."

"No, you did not. You said consummate. That's what you do on your wedding night."

Buster blinked.

"Is that a proposal?"

Sissie picked up the menu and hit him upside the head with it.

"You're a long way from France, so unless there's something else you'd rather have, I'll bring you some tomato soup."

Buster whispered to Levi, "I think she likes me."

Damn it was hard to hold that boy's attention.

"Speaking of proposals, Buster," I said, "Have I got a dandy one for you."

"I don't think I want to hear this," he muttered.

"Sure you do," said Levi as he turned and glared at me. "As a matter of fact, so do I."

"What I got in mind is this. I'll do you a little favor if you do me one."

Buster was watching Sissy's every move. "You know the first girl I ever kissed was a redhead."

"Buster!" I yelled. "Pay attention. I said, I want to do you a favor."

"What's the favor?" Buster looked suspicious.

"I'd like to come out and shoe those two man-killing broomtails of yours."

Now, Buster was real good atop of a horse, but he wasn't worth spit underneath one. He'd rather take a bath in lye soap than shoe his own horses. Specially those two demons. There was only two men in the county that could get near them. Me and Bud Thompson. Bud usually did the job because I was on the road most of the time.

"You want to shoe my horses?"

"That's right. I know ole Bud's in Kremling, so I'm offering to do it for you."

"That Communist! What's he doing in Russia?"

"Bud ain't no Communist," Levi said. "What the hell are you talking about?"

"Hoss is the one that said he's in the Kremlin. Not me!"

"I said Kremling! Kremling, Colorado, you fool! That's where his sister lives."

"Oh."

Sissie brought Buster's hot dog and soup and set them down in front of him.

"You boys need anything else?" she asked sweetly.

19

"Where's my compliments?" Buster asked.

"I'm not giving you any compliments. What would I give you a compliment for?"

"For my hot dog. That's what!"

"Why would I give you a compliment for your hot dog? You didn't cook it?"

"Hell, you mean a man has to cook his own hot dog to get compliments for it?"

Levi and I lost it. Even though we were used to Buster, watching him try to impress the new girl in town — and an English major at that — well, it got us to laughing and slapping the table so hard, the ole lady in the next booth hollered for us to shut up.

I pointed to the counter and sputtered, "I think he wants the mustard."

"Well, why didn't he just ask for it?"

Sissie stomped over to the counter.

"Damn, she's disagreeable!" Levi said.

"I think she's nice," muttered Buster. "She probably just needs a good man around to make her happy. Somebody like me."

Sissie brought a jar of mustard over and slammed it on the table in front of him.

"Here's your condiment!" she shouted at him.

"I don't know why you're so mad about . . ."

I put my hand over Buster's mouth.

"Buster, just forget it. We've got business to take care of. Remember?"

"Okay. So, what kind of favor do you want from me, Hoss?"

"Does your Mom still work at that beauty parlor?"

"Yup."

"Think you can borrow a long black wig from her?"

"Wait a minute! What the hell are you up to?"

"We need you to borrow a wig."

"And a couple of other things," Levi grinned.

"Is that all? You just want to borrow some stuff?"

I winked at him. "We need just one more little thing, pard."

"I don't like that look on your face. What else?"

"We need you to dress up."

Half of Buster's hot dog shot out of his mouth.

"Dress up?" he choked.

"Just for an hour or two."

"Forget it! It ain't Halloween and I ain't wearing no wig."

Levi shrugged like he was ready to give up. But not me. I was already making plans for the concert.

"That's too bad, Buster. I was just thinking about the last time you tried to shoe them old nags of yours and how that old bay tore your shirt off. Right after he ripped the barn door off . . . and right after he broke your foot and right after . . ."

"Hold it! Hold it!" Levi came back to life. "Look, Buster. Would it help if I told you we was planning a little surprise for one of them Yankee Prairie Dogs?"

All of a sudden Buster had a whole new outlook on the situation.

"Well, why didn't you say so?"

Levi poked me in the ribs like "ain't I smart."

"That's more like it," I said to Buster. "I knew you'd come around after awhile."

"Well, you should've told me the part about them Yankees first. So, tell me what is it you want me to do?"

"See, this here assistant teacher thinks we're taking him to get a glimpse of the lost tribe of the Pecos."

"There ain't no lost tribe of the Pecos."

"We know that," I said. "That's the surprise."

"Oh." Buster slurped his soup.

"And you're going to be Pecos Man."

When I told him I wanted him to dress up in the wig and find a piece of cowhide for a loin cloth, I thought he'd swaller his spoon.

"And you need a fishing spear," Levi told him.

"You can't catch fish in the Pecos with a spear. Hell, you can't even see one in that muddy ole water. It ain't but about six inches deep. You two are plum crazy."

Levi gave me a hopeless look.

"It's make believe," I said. "Besides, I didn't say you had to catch any fish. Did I?"

"No. Anything else?"

"Don't forget to wear a little war paint," I said.

"Don't I get a headrest and a paint horse?"

This was going to be harder than I thought. All of a sudden Buster wanted to be some kind of movie star.

"No, you're supposed to look like you belong to a lost tribe, Buster. Not Sitting Bull!"

"I know a little a Cherokee," he grinned. "That ought to come in handy."

"No!" Levi hollered. "You aren't gonna say anything. Just grunt a little."

"All right," Buster agreed at last. "I guess I can do that all right."

"We're going to meet the professor here at seven tomorrow morning," I told him. "So we'll stop by your place about six to make sure you got your costume together. Then you drive out there where we used to party. About a mile and a half past that flat outside of Roswell."

"And be sure to park far away," Levi reminded him, "So no one can see your truck."

Buster was beaming. "Hey, this might be fun after all."

Levi and I put our hats on.

"See you in the morning, Buster," I said. "Six o'clock. Don't forget."

22

"I won't forget." He waved at us and hollered at Sissie. "Hey, Sissie! You all got any of that tappy yoka pudding left?"

The next morning about five thirty I shook ole Levi. "Wake up, pard. We have a date with destiny."

At that point, I think the both of us was wishing we'd volunteered to show Phillip something nocturnal like vampire bats. But it was too late for that. We stopped by the bootlegger's for a couple of sixpacks — Portales was dry as a bone in those days — and headed straight for Buster's place.

I was thinking I might have to wake Buster up, but every light in the house was on when we got there. We didn't even get a chance to knock. As soon as we got up on the porch, he swung the door open and stood there with his arms in the air, swiveling his hips like a hula dancer.

"What do you think, Hoss?"

He just had to ask. Me and Levi took one look and started laughing so loud I thought for sure we'd wake everybody in the neighborhood. He was wearing a red wig which was tied on with a shoestring from a pair of work boots, and there was three big turkey feathers sticking up in the back. He had plastered some kind of sparkly red lipstick across his cheeks and hung one flowered dishtowel from a skinny white belt around his middle. Another one was hanging in the back. I could not believe my eyes.

"Holy shit, Buster! I said a black wig, not red for godssake. And what's with the shiny lipstick?"

"Mom didn't have a black wig. This ain't red either. It's auburn. She said the Brassy Bronze lipstick shows off the bronze highlights in the wig."

"Damn! You ain't supposed to be some Las Vegas showgirl, Buster. Take that . . ."

23

"The wig and the lipstick are the least of our problems," Levi interrupted. "Buster, you can't wear dishtowels. Where's the cowhide?"

"I couldn't find any. Besides, these here at least cover up my butt and ... you know what I mean. I don't want to parade around half naked in front of a stranger."

I looked over at Levi.

"Man, we're going to need more beer. If Phillip ain't drunk as a skunk when he sees this, the Pecos Tribe will become extinct before the end of the day."

Levi was standing there with his mouth open like there was no hope. Then, all of a sudden he busted out laughing.

"He don't look that damn funny, Levi."

"Hell, I ain't laughing at him any more. I'm laughing at you."

"What the hell for?"

"I'm glad you asked, Mr. Cecil B. De Mille," Levi smirked. "You're so busy being a big Hollywood producer, you haven't even noticed our real problem." He pointed to Buster's legs. "You can't get a man drunk enough to miss that."

Buster had a typical cowboy tan. He was brown as toast from the waist up, but his legs would have glowed in the dark.

"I was just going to get to that, smart alec!" I said.

"Right! And what are you going to do about this?"

Levi walked up to Buster and pulled a curly hair from his chest.

"Ow!" Buster hollered. "Don't do that! Don't you know this here is manly? The women love it."

"Not Indian women," Levi snapped. "You damn fool. Indians don't have chest hair."

Buster looked at me like he was waiting for me tell him Levi was lying.

"He's right, Buster. They don't. I swear, it's true."

24

Buster wasn't buying it.

"Hold it! I am not shaving my chest."

"That so," I said. "You sure you want to shoe them horses yourself, then? 'Cause I don't care. I'm a very busy man you know."

Levi snickered while Buster stood there pondering. Just when you think you know a guy, that's when you find out you really don't. I thought Buster was the perfect one to recruit for our special production. Usually he'd go along with everyone else and didn't ask too many questions. He was what you might call . . . well, I guess you'd say he was easily persuaded. So, you can imagine how surprised me and Levi was when he came up with one of them there ultimatums.

"Okay, I'll do it. But only on one condition."

Levi and I looked at each other in disbelief. As far as we knew, it was the first time Buster had ever engaged in any negotiations.

"You got to shoe my horses the rest of the summer, Hoss. Not just this once."

"Forget it!" I said.

Levi jabbed me in the ribs.

"You better think about that, Hoss. We're running out of time. You got the world's next most famous archeologist just waiting for you to hand him the discovery of a lifetime. You sure you want to miss that? And what about the concert?"

Damn that Levi! He had a point, though. Them Buck Owen tickets was growing scarcer by the minute. I decided to negotiate.

"Forget it, Buster. I ain't shoeing horses all summer."

"And I ain't shaving my chest."

"Now, what are you going to do, Hoss?"

Levi was starting to lose his patience.

25

"We'll tell Phillip that the Pecos Man is a direct descendant of Cro Magnon Man and that he sheds in the late summer."

"Cro ... Cro Mag ..." Buster was trying his dam'dest to remember where he'd heard that name before. "Isn't that one of them there sororities at the college?"

"Never mind," I told him. "Save that intellectual bullshit for Sissie. Where'd you get them dishtowels?"

"In the kitchen in the middle drawer?"

"You got any more?"

"Oh yeah. Mom brings that kind of junk over all the time."

"Let's go in the kitchen. Levi, you dig through that drawer and see if you can find some towels that don't have flowers on them. Look for a solid color. Especially brown or something."

Levi started rummaging through the drawer, and that's when I saw Buster's boots under the kitchen chair where he'd kicked them off. I pointed to the boots.

"Buster! You got any shoe polish that color?"

"Yeah. It's in that cupboard up there."

"Look here, Hoss," said Levi as he pulled three tan-colored towels out of the drawer. "How's this?"

Our luck was improving. They even matched.

"That's fine. We just need two of them."

"What's the polish for?" asked Buster. "I wasn't counting on shining my boots this morning."

"You're fixing to get a suntan, Buster."

"Ah, er I ..."

Ole Buster really went to stammering when I grabbed a butcher knife off the counter.

"Okay, okay!" he squeaked.

I guess he didn't realize that all I wanted to do was perform a little operation on them towels. I started slicing and he let out a big ole sigh. He was so relieved to find out I wasn't going to cut him up, he didn't say a word. But he got a little concerned when I went to painting his legs with the shoe polish.

"This stuff'll come off, won't it?"

I looked at Levi and shrugged.

"Well, if it don't," Levi chuckled, "You'll have the best tan in town."

"I'll have the only tan in town."

"What can I say?" Levi said. "Some men got it and some men don't. That's why ole Hoss there ain't got a steady girlfriend. It's them skinny white legs of his."

Ordinarily them was fighting words, but I was too busy creating the missing link to take time out to fight with Levi.

Fifteen minutes later Buster looked more like a member of the Pecos Tribe than one of the tribe their selves. Providing there had actually been a Pecos Tribe, that is. Yessir. He was definitely a fine-looking specimen.

"There!" I stood back to admire my handiwork. "You're all set, Buster. Now, just one more thing. Let me hear you grunt."

Buster sounded more like some ole boy reading the newspaper in the can.

"I guess that'll work. We don't have time for speech training. Let's head out, Levi. Buster, we'll see you at the river. Now, when you see us coming, I want you to wade out there in the river with your spear and start fishing. And don't forget to grunt. Let me hear you do that again."

I thought Levi was going to wet his pants. And I could hardly keep a straight face myself.

"That's fine. You're all set."

"Wait! My spear."

Buster reached inside the kitchen pantry and pulled out an old broom handle with an ice pick he'd duct-taped to the bottom. Levi lost it again. He started laughing so hard he had to sit down.

"Damn, Buster!" I said. "Don't you know what a spear is? Why couldn't you put a knife blade on the end of that stick?"

"I only got one good knife, and I never did know what this damn thing was for anyway."

He started unwrapping the tape.

"Forget it, Hoss." Levi was all serious again. "Put that tape back on there, Buster. We got to go."

"You're right for once, Levi."

I hadn't forgot his unkind remark about my legs, but this was no time to disagree.

I hollered to Buster: "Be careful with that damn thing, Buster. We'll see you out there in three hours."

"Three hours? It's only an hour and a half away."

"I know that. But Phillip thinks we're taking him far into the wilds somewhere. So, we're taking the scenic route."

"There ain't nothing scenic out there."

"You just let me worry about that. Get going."

Buster straightened up his new skirt and waved, and me and Levi hopped into the truck and headed for the cafe to pick up Phillip.

"Boy, Hoss, I sure hope ole Buster gassed up last night. If he runs out of fuel, it'll be a long walk. Nobody in their right mind would stop for a hitchhiker wearing that get-up."

"Oh, he'd get a ride all right. Straight to the loony bin."

We were only about ten minutes late to the cafe. I saw Phillip's car outside, but he wasn't in it. No surprise, though. He was inside eating, and he wasn't hard to spot. He was wearing cargo shorts, kneesocks and lace-up boots, and the wildest Hawaiian floweredy shirt I ever saw.

When Levi and me walked up to his table, he was just polishing off the Rancho Special — a T-bone steak, four eggs, half a pound of hash browns and two biscuits.

I took a suspicious look around the room, then leaned over ole Phillip and whispered: "You ready to go you know where?"

"You bet!" He drank his glass of milk in two gulps. "I just need to get some things out of the car."

We followed him out to the parking lot and watched as he opened the door and reached across the seat for his gear. He put two cameras and a pair of binoculars around his neck and a leather satchel over his shoulder. Then he reached back in and grabbed a suitcase.

"Phillip, you don't need no suitcase," I told him. "We ain't spending the night."

"This isn't a suitcase. It's my tape recorder."

"Oh. Well, come on. Let's go."

"Just a minute. I have to get the rest of my things out of the trunk. Will you guys help me, please?"

Levi shook his head and muttered to me. "Damn, Hoss! What else does that idiot need?"

Phillip opened the trunk and pulled out the biggest thermos ever built. He handed it to Levi, grabbed another suitcase, and then gave me a big ole grocery sack.

I took the sack. That sucker weighed at least ten pounds. I figured he must have packed enough for all of us. And Buster, too. I just had to open it. Inside was a bag of apples, six sandwiches, three packages of cupcakes, two bags of potato chips, a bag of bridge mix, a jar of pickles and a tin of Spanish peanuts.

"Holy shit, Phillip! There's enough food in here to feed the Kettle Family."

"Didn't you guys tell me to pack a lunch?"

I slapped him on the back.

"Well, I didn't mean for you to pack one for us, too. That was just downright thoughtful of you, Phillip. I thank you."

Levi shoved the thermos in my hand and snatched the bag away from me.

"The peanuts are mine!" He reached in, pulled out the peanut tin and stuffed it inside his shirt.

We tried to squeeze Phillip and all his stuff in the pickup, but there was no way.

"Some of this has to go in the back," Levi said as he tossed the tape recorder into the bed of the truck."

"Hey! That's delicate equipment!" shrieked Phillip, pointing to a sixpack that already had one bottle missing. "Can't we put these in the back instead?"

"No!" Levi said. "That's all that stands between us and dying of thirst out in the desert."

"Just consider that our first-aid kit," I said reassuringly. "Now, why don't you just jump in there, Phillip, and make yourself all comfy like."

Phillip's big ole butt nearly filled half the seat. I could tell by the pathetic look in his eyes that he knew there was no way to get comfortable in that pickup, specially with that sixpack staring up at him. He was nervous as a cat, and when Levi hopped in and squeezed him between the two of us, he got real scared. For a minute there I thought he was going to jump back out of the truck. Levi didn't look too comfortable himself. He was squished so hard up against the door his shoulders were knocking together. It was only about seventy miles to our destination and I was wishing that was all the further I had to drive. But we had told Phillip we'd be on the road three hours, so I just kept on driving. Of course, I had no way of telling how far or how fast we were going because the speedometer was busted. Besides that, the roads out there were dirt. Heck, some weren't even roads. Just cow trails.

After awhile Phillip said he was positive we had gone three hundred miles. That was all we needed to hear. I stopped the truck right there in the middle of the road, and Levi grabbed the church key and proceeded to open our refreshments.

"Here, you go Phillip." Levi handed him a beer. "This one's on the house."

"It's a little early to be drinking." He looked over to me and then at Levi. "Isn't it?"

"Believe me, Phillip, we're all gonna be a whole lot more comfortable if we have a few cold ones."

Levi was right again.

"Well, okay," Phillip said kind of timid like.

I headed the truck down the road again, driving as fast as I could and praying that I wouldn't break an axle, or worse yet, hit the ditch and bust up Phillip's delicate equipment. That ole boy developed a taste for beer real quick. Every time I hit a pothole and he slid over and mashed Levi up against the door, he'd laugh like he couldn't quit. Levi took it for awhile, but he darn sure wasn't enjoying it.

"Watch them damn holes, Hoss!"

"Okay, Levi. But I ain't got no control over Phillip here. I can't hold onto the wheel and him too. He's a real handful."

"Yee-ouch!" Levi screamed as Phillip went sliding in his direction again.

I don't think Phillip had drank a lot of beer before. After a few swallers he was giddy as a virgin on her first date. I'm sure he didn't notice that we had started driving in circles. He was yacking so much me and Levi couldn't get a word in sideways. He told us how famous he was going to be and how all the other student professors would be jealous when he got interviewed on the Cleveland radio station. I kept on driving round and

31

round, and after a couple more beers I needed to make a pit stop.

"Okay, Phillip, let's start scouting here. But you got to be real quiet. I need to make a little trip in the weeds over there. I'll be right back."

First I grabbed Phillip's thermos. I was worried about how convincing Buster was going to be, and I didn't want our famous archeologist suddenly sobering up on us. I watched Levi help Phillip gather all his gear. Then the two of them climbed up a little sand hill with a couple of bushes on the top. It's a darn good thing they weren't trying to sneak up on anybody. You could've heard Phillip's junk jingling and jangling a mile away.

As soon as I was out of sight, I emptied the thermos in the sand and headed back for the truck. Phillip had flopped down on his belly and parked his nose under his binoculars. He was looking one way and then the other. Levi had laid down beside him. He was on his back with his arms crossed behind his head and his hat pulled down over his face like he was going to take a nap. I put the thermos in the truck, then hurried over to the hill quiet as I could.

I kicked Levi's boots.

"Did you forget you're on official business?"

"I figured ole Phillip there could take first watch," Levi yawned.

"I don't see a thing," Phillip whispered.

"Sometimes they're hard to find," I whispered back to him. "But don't worry. Me and ole Levi here have tracked them before. We'll find them."

"I'm hungry," Phillip said. "Want a sandwich?"

Before we could answer, he was making a beeline for the truck and clanging just like a bell.

"Come on," I said to Levi. "We got to rendezvous with Buster. Let's load Phillip up and go."

"I don't know if he's had enough beer yet. I had a hard time getting him to drink that last one. He said he wanted a cup of coffee."

"Don't worry about the coffee." I grinned and pulled my hat down over my eyes. "I took care of that little problem."

By the time we got to the truck, Phillip had downed a sandwich and half a bag of chips already. This was one man I would never want to get stranded with. If you was to run out of groceries, you might just become somebody's favorite snack. Like they did at the Donner Party.

"Here you are, Levi." Phillip held out his grocery sack. "You boys want some lunch?"

"No, no. Not now." We shook our heads.

"Boy those chips are salty!" Phillip started rummaging around in the truck. "Where's my thermos?"

When he found it, he unscrewed the top, tipped it up and cried like a baby.

"It's empty!"

"Hell, yes," I said. "You polished that sucker off twenty minutes ago."

Levi looked surprised, but nothing close to how Phillip looked. Levi handed him a bottle of beer.

"Here. You look like you could use a drink."

Phillip shrugged and took a sip. After he finished off the potato chips, he emptied the rest of the bottle in one swaller.

I was anxious to get the show back on the road, so I whispered real excited like to Phillip: "I think I just heard the Indians. They must be headed for their other fishing hole. Let's go see."

"All right. But I'm still thirsty. Can I have another beer?"

"Sure!" Levi grinned as he cranked the top off another bottle.

33

We loaded up the gear and headed for the spot where Buster was supposed to meet us. I parked the truck about a quarter mile from our meeting spot and reminded Phillip again to be quiet. After eating like a horse, he was starting to sound like one. He was a-huffing and a-puffing, and weaving awful bad, too. But, even without all that noise, he couldn't have snuck up on a dead man. That flowered shirt would have made King Tut rise from his tomb.

Meanwhile, me and Levi tromped on every dry twig we could so Buster would recognize us. He would have been spooked if all he heard was Phillip, and we sure didn't want him running off now. We led the way up a hill and crouched next to some brush while we waited for Phillip. When he finally caught up with us, he had to adjust all that gear around his neck before he could sit down.

I pointed toward the river and whispered: "This is one of their favorite fishing holes. I think that's one of them down there. Take a look, Phillip."

Phillip squatted down beside us, wallered out a spot for himself, and peeked up over the bush. He got so excited trying to unwind his camera that he tipped over and rolled halfway back down the hill. But he wasn't going to give up that easy. Puffing and a-panting, he waddled back up and took another look. When he spotted Buster he grinned so big, I swear a B52 could have flown in his mouth and landed on his tongue.

Buster was there in all his glory, standing in about five or six inches of water, poking at it with his spear just like he knew what he was doing. He spun around and grunted like a pig, then waded in the opposite direction and poked some more. I have to admit, he was putting on one helluva show. I couldn't have acted out that role any better if I'd tried it. There was only one problem. The shoe polish was starting to wash off and Phillip was grabbing at the straps around his neck.

"What are you doing, Phillip?"

"My binoculars. I want a closer look."

"Don't!" I held his arm. "If that savage sees the reflection off that glass, he'll go crazy. And you know what that means."

"What?"

From the look on his face, I thought that beer had drowned his brain.

"We're all dead men!" Levi said.

"Oooh." Phillip sounded very solemn. "Can I go get my recorder, then?"

"I wouldn't if I were you," Levi said. "Them Indians have ears like coyotes and they're dead shots with them spears."

Phillip looked disappointed. He turned back to watch Pecos Man stabbing at the water, and all of a sudden Buster let out a yell.

"Shee-iit!"

That knot head had stabbed himself with his damned ice pick.

"What did he say?"

Phillip was in shock. I had to think fast.

"Sheetae," I said. "In Pecos, that means I got one."

"Really?"

"Really!"

Phillip pulled out a notebook and started writing. That was a relief, because Buster had commenced to jumping up and down with his foot in his hand and making some noises that I couldn't have translated without cracking up. Instead, I kept Phillip occupied with some real astonishing Pecos Tribe folklore while Levi sent some not-too-intelligent signals to Buster. He was trying for all he was worth to make him get out the water and leave, but our buddy had been bitten by the star bug and he wasn't finished performing for us yet.

35

Buster finally got Levi's message just as Phillip turned around to see his Pecos Man running up the bank.

"That man has white feet!" he gasped.

"Oh my God! Look, Levi. It's Chief Whitefoot."

"Who?" Phillip asked.

"Chief Whitefoot," Levi repeated. "He's the fiercest one of the bunch."

"He's right, Phillip. That's the leader of the warriors. This is your lucky day."

"Oh my gawd!"

About that time Buster let out a whoop, struck a match on a big rock, and threw it on top of a pile of old leaves and sticks. Phillip was so intrigued, he never even asked where a wild Indian would get a match. I guess you could say I was a little intrigued myself. But I didn't have to wonder long. Buster pulled his saddle blanket out of the bushes and started fanning the fire. I'm sure he intended to make smoke signals, like they do in the movies, but I don't think he had counted on getting so close to the fire. When his blanket started smoldering, he got so excited he threw it on the ground and stomped on it with his wounded foot. I guess that hurt a whole bunch because that war dance of his looked purty danged authentic to me.

Meanwhile, Phillip was pestering me for more Indian history than I could dream up. I was just about to tell him about their language when he heard ole Pecos Man start hollering. No doubt about it, Buster was mad. Real mad. In fact, he went to cussing so bad I was wishing I had some earplugs for Phillip.

"Did you hear that?" Phillip cupped his hand around his ear. "It sounds like he's saying . . ."

Levi grabbed one of Phillip's arms, I grabbed the other, and we spun him around like a top.

"Hey, you guys. This is important. Where's my tape recorder? I want to know what he's saying."

"I'll tell you what he's saying," Levi growled. "Attack the white men! That's what he's saying."

"And that smoke is going to signal the rest of the tribe to come after us," I added. "We got to get the hell out of here. Now!"

That was the truth! With a wounded foot and his good saddle blanket a-blazing, Buster was liable to come after our hides at any moment. Levi and me helped gather up all that crap again and we headed back to the truck. We had a helluva time trying to get Phillip to shut up. It was worse than minding a two-year-old.

"When can we go back? Can you take me back there tomorrow? Why not? I'm going to rent a movie camera the next time. How about next week?"

"No!" Levi shouted when he'd had enough of Phillip's whining. "We can't go back, so you just better forget it."

"But, I don't understand," Phillip persisted.

"Because if we go back," I said, "Either they'll move camp so they won't be discovered again, or they'll be waiting to ambush us. I ain't taking the chance."

Phillip was quiet for the first time all day. He didn't say a word until we got back to the Wagon Wheel parking lot.

"Now, Phillip." I talked like I was his kindeegarten teacher. "Remember what I told you. You can't say anything about this or all your schoolmates will horn in on your discovery."

"I can't tell anybody?"

"No one. But, there is one thing you can do. When you get back home, why don't you write it up in one of them journals you boys subscribe to?"

"Of course. What a splendid idea!" Phillip was genuinely pleased with that idea. "And don't worry, I'll give you guys credit for all your work, too."

"Oh no. You got to promise not to do that."

"Why?"

"Yeah," Levi grinned. "Why?"

"Because it'd ruin our love life."

"Ruin what?"

"You heard me. If you was to put me and Levi's name in that article, well . . . the girls who read it, they'd start thinking me and Levi was as smart as you and . . . I hate to say it Phillip, but the women around here ain't attracted to the genius type. You know what I mean?"

Phillip shrugged. "Yes, I do. Unfortunately. Well, gentlemen, it's been a great adventure just the same. You really went to a lot of trouble and I want you to know, I do appreciate it. Thank you."

For a minute I thought he was going to run off without paying up.

"What about our tickets, Phillip?"

"Oh yes. They're right here." He pulled them out of his sweaty shirt pocket and smiled. "Thanks again."

We all shook hands and that was the last time me and Levi ever saw ole Phillip. We got to see Buck and his Buckaroos that weekend, though, and then we headed out to the rodeo in Lubbock. I won a second is saddle broncs and Levi won a third in bull riding. It seemed like we'd hit a lick, and for a change, we actually came home with a few dollars in our pockets.

Naturally, the Wagon Wheel Cafe was the first stop we made when we got back in town. That was the best place to go when you had to catch up on the latest news, and we didn't have to wait too long before we heard what we was hoping to hear. Two ole boys were huddled in a booth discussing some familiar territory up near Roswell where they'd gone to a dance. Seems they spotted some of them Yankee Prairie Dogs up there and they was combing the flats for Indian treasure. According-ing to one feller, they was plum obsessed with tracking down some damn Indian they called a Pecos Man. The next day we found out that ole Phillip had decided to go back up there on his own, but he never could find the exact same spot and he ended up getting lost. Took a ten-man search party and a pair of my Pa's hounds to track him down.

Well, you know how little towns and greedy grave robbers are. Soon as word got out, them fellow students of Phillip's couldn't hardly wait to get up there and make their own discoveries. They didn't discover much, of course, but they sure enough tore up them sand hills. In fact, they made such a racket and stirred up the dust so bad, the real prairie dogs moved out.

After our adventure with Phillip, Levi was plum disgusted with all them cranky, sunburned bone diggers hanging around. But I got to thinking that the whole affair might just be the business opportunity him and me was waiting for.

"You know, Levi, we could make a chunk a money off these smart types."

"How's that?"

"Did you forget already?"

"Forget what?"

"How excited ole Phillip was when we took him on that little adventure? Hell, we can start a packing outfit. We can take them ole boys to see the Pecos Tribe. For a charge, of course."

"Hoss, you're as crazy as they are. Did you forget there ain't no Pecos Tribe?"

"No. But we don't need a whole tribe. It worked for Phillip, didn't it?"

"Where you gonna get an Indian this time? You know you can't drag Buster out of the Wagon Wheel. He's in there every spare moment trying to talk Sissie into marrying him. Hell, he's even going to the library every day to impress her. I heard he checked out some Hummingway and things like that."

"Checked out some what? You know that boy can't read worth spit."

"I know that. But he takes them in the cafe and pretends he's reading. I guess Sissie don't know the difference."

"She knows the difference all right. Trouble is, she probably don't care and he's too dumb to know the difference."

"Maybe so. But, you don't want to see ole Buster that bad anyway, do you Hoss?"

I had to admit it. I was not looking forward to catching up with Buster. Not on account of he was still mad about stabbing his foot and burning his good saddle blanket and all. It was them horses of his. Damn I hated myself for making that promise to him.

"You're right, Levi. We probably couldn't pull it off without Buster."

When I couldn't come up with another idiot to play Buster's part, I gave up on my idea. I guess one Pecos Man was more than them archeologists could imagine, anyhow. They went back to studying the Clovis Man instead, and by the end of the summer they had opened the Blackwater Drawer Museum out there on Highway 70 headed to Clovis. They put all the stuff they had dug up in there, but it closed down almost as soon as it opened. I heard they forgot about one important incidental — money to pay the light bill. Of course, Portales ain't exactly a popular vacation spot, and the tourists that came through town that year sure didn't line up to get in their museum. I saw a few of them stop to take pictures of the big ole mastodon and some other critters painted on the front side of the building, but I don't remember anybody going in there.

I didn't lose any sleep over the museum, of course, but I did feel kind of sorry for Phillip when I found out he had dropped out of school that fall. He went into business for himself, according to one of his archeologist buddies. Evidently inherited some money and opened his own burger joint. It's called Pecos Pete's. As for me and Levi, we been trying to find an excuse to visit Cleveland for years. You never know. We might just stop in and say "Hey" someday if we ever get back that way.

Look Who's Talking

The only people I know that like driving night and day are truckers. And I think a lot of them ain't all that fond of it. Well, I ain't exactly fond of it either, but I can drive if I have to. Eating the same thing every day, or skipping a meal now and then ain't exactly fun, but the driving don't bother me none. No sir. I guess you could say the worst part of traveling all the time is the lack of personal hygiene, if you know what I mean. When I was rodeoing, I did most of my traveling in the Southwest. There was a few decent rest areas and truck stops near the big cities in them days, but a lot of the rodeos weren't anywhere near a big city. Hell, there's places in Texas and New Mexico where you could drive two hundred miles without seeing a tree — even a little sapling for a dog to water. And finding a place for a grown man to tidy up is near impossible. That was exactly the situation I found myself in one summer.

☆ ☆ ☆

Me and an ole boy named Cody had been to three rodeos in a week and neither one of us had a bath in four days. That was one time I was glad my car didn't have air conditioning. We was traveling across the Texas panhandle, and if it wasn't for the fresh air blowing in all four windows, we'd both been dead from asphyxiation. Now Cody wasn't a bad ole boy, and he really didn't smell any worse than any other cowboy would have after four days on the road. But he was no conversationalist. Ordinarily I would have picked another partner to travel with, but since I'd been running with him I had placed in every show. And so had he. I guess I kind of figured he was my good luck charm.

A lot of the time, the old rigs we drove back then didn't even have brakes, let alone a radio. So a man depended on his traveling companion to keep him entertained — and awake. Cody didn't do either one. I might have expected that from an old cowboy. They'd generally rather sleep than gab. But Cody was only about twenty years old. I thought he'd have at least one good tale to tell, especially when I started repeating my own stories over to myself. I tried every way I knew to get that boy to speak up.

"Say Cody, that sure was a purty ride you put on that bull last night."

He just nodded.

"Was he tough to ride?"

"Yep."

"He looked double stout. Did he jerk you around much?"

"Nope."

I'm telling you, it was frustrating as hell to try to talk to him.

"Who are you? Gary Cooper's son?"

Cody looked at me confused for a minute and then he said: "Nope."

I thought I'd be clever and ask him a question that he couldn't answer with yes or no. "I heard your older brother used to be a bull-dogger. How many brothers and sisters you got?"

He held up four fingers.

I gave up and drank another beer. By the time we got to the next town — about an hour and a half later — he was still silent and I had polished off a sixer. It was two o'clock in the afternoon and I was hot, hungry, dirty and bored. Dirty and bored tied for first place. So, I guess you can just imagine how happy I was when I saw that little ole truck stop up ahead.

"Look at that, Cody! It's time to shut her down."

"Chow!" he screeched, which was just about as much noise as I'd heard him make all day.

"Chow hell!" I hollered. "You're gonna hit them showers."

"Me? What about you?"

I thought ole Cody was on a roll for a minute there.

"You first, pard. I've been to this place before. Their menu fits on one page and they only have one shower. I'll take a little siesta while you're in there and then I'll take my turn. After that we can both get something to eat."

I pulled into a little grocery store next to the truck stop and parked under a tree — the only one in town. Cody gave me a funny look like the heat had gone to my head.

"It's only a block," I said. "You can see the truck stop from here. I told you I'm gonna take myself a little nap while you're hosing off. Do you see any other shade trees?"

"Nope."

I pinched my nose with my thumb and forefinger.

"Hurry up, dammit! You're getting riper by the minute standing there in that sun."

Cody did as he was told and grabbed the shower bag. It was the brown paper variety with the bare necessities — a bar of Dial soap, a bottle of Old Spice after shave, a razor and a couple of towels. I leaned back in the seat and pulled my hat down over my eyes. I was just getting comfortable when I realized I had drunk entirely too much beer to be settling down for a nap.

It sure enough was a relief to hear the shower pounding when I walked into the men's room. That meant we could roll the windows up tonight on our way to Lubbock. That is, if it ever cooled down below eighty. Cody's clothes were all wadded up on the bench and he was humming a tune to hisself. I couldn't tell what tune it was because he didn't sing any songs with words either. I guessed he didn't hear me come in. He just kept a-humming the whole time I was watering the trough.

To this day I don't know what come over me at that moment. I didn't even think of it until I was standing there in front of the urinal, but the next thing I knew I was gathering up every stitch of clothes in that heap — Cody's jeans, his boots, his shirt, and even those filthy shorts — and I took off for the car like I was being chased by a bear.

I wasn't sleepy any more. I could hardly wait for ole Cody to come a-streaking out of there. Somehow I just knew he was going to have more words to say besides yep and nope. It took awhile for him to figure out that nobody — me least of all — was coming in there to save him. But it was worth the wait. First I saw him peek out and look over toward the gas pumps. He pulled back real quick and the second time his ole head popped out, he looked north and south. Soon as he got a bead on the grocery store parking lot he came high-stepping it out of there like a Tennessee Walker.

I couldn't believe what I was seeing. I must have dropped his belt on the men's room floor. It was pulled tight around his middle and he had tucked paper towels under it so that they hung down in front and back. In fact, they was all around him. It looked like some kind of disposable hula skirt. That pavement had to be real hot because he came prancing across there on his tippy toes like he was a one-man street performance of the Swan Lake Ballet.

I was laughing so hard I barely could see, but Cody was traveling fast. I sure didn't want to miss the show, so I wiped my tears on my shirt, and when I looked up, there he was barreling down the sidewalk.

About halfway between the truck stop and the grocery store, one of them paper towels came loose and fluttered to the ground. Cody bent over to pick it up and two more fell out. He tried moving a bit faster and another one bit the dust. For every towel he tried to retrieve, he lost two more. By the time he had reached the parking lot, there was more empty spots than there was towels. Cody looked down to make sure he wasn't revealing his manhood, and wouldn't you know it, he ran smack dab into a little old lady coming out of the store. She landed on the sidewalk and her groceries spilt all over the parking lot.

"Oooh!" She took one look at Cody and screamed like she was being attacked by a savage beast.

That poor little woman had been run over by a naked man and Cody didn't know if he should help her to her feet, round up her groceries, or just run like hell. Now, if he had just said he was sorry and moved along ... but I already told you how it is with him and words. So there he stood hovering over her, naked as a jaybird, trying to decide what to do next.

"I'm sorry," he said at last. "Can I help you up?"

Cody was talking! Even if it wasn't to me.

The ole gal didn't much appreciate his offer, though. When she screamed again and he saw the store manager coming, he started heading my way with those paper towels just a-flying.

I locked the car doors when I saw the look on his face. I was afraid he'd try to kill me. He only had one towel left and it was not strategically located. I had to let him in. We couldn't afford to get arrested. Not for nudity!

When he seen the door was locked, that's when the dam burst. Beginning with a one-sided discussion of my ancestral heritage, Cody let loose on me like he was the county judge.

"You low-life! How would you like somebody to do that to you? Did you see that old woman? She thought I was some kind of mad rapist. I should have believed all them ole boys that warned me about you. They told me not to go down the road with you. Now that I think about it, I should have figured it out for myself. You even look like a suspicious character with them shifty eyes of yours. It ain't worth it! If this is what I got to put up with to be on the rodeo circuit, forget it!"

Cody hadn't even drawn a breath. And I don't think he was finished talking yet, but I took a chance and interrupted him anyhow.

"Just look who's talking now," I said with my very best shit-eating grin.

Once Cody got started, I couldn't shut him up. It wouldn't be polite to repeat all of what he had to say. Hell, I'd probably blush telling it. But, he made it purty dang clear that he didn't want to go down the road with me again. In fact, he insisted on me driving him straight to his uncle's house in San Angelo.

I guess I couldn't blame him for wanting to be rid of me. I would have killed any ole boy that pulled a prank on me like that.

Anyway, I was looking forward to having a new traveling companion. Me and Jake was planning to meet up in Snyder the following week. The bad part was that Cody and me were still aways from San Angelo, so for the next couple of days I had to take my showers with my clothes on.

Paybacks are hell, aren't they?

Off the Hook

If you want to see a wreck in the making, find two cowboys that have spent their whole life on the high desert, take them into the mountains, and set them down by a lake. And if you want to really confuse them, hand them each a fishing pole and a sixpack. What happens next is the stuff legends are made of.

☆ ☆ ☆

Levi and me grew up in Roosevelt County, New Mexico. Lake Roosevelt is a mud puddle outside the fire station. That's how much we knew about lakes and fishing. I believe it was the summer of 65. We were on the road, and broke again as usual, when Levi got one of them strokes of genius that he was so famous for.

"Hoss, I got an idea to save us some money."

"All seventeen dollars and forty-six cents of it?"

"No, we'll need that for beer. I'm talking about all them other expenses. I know where we can get some eats and a place to stay for free."

"Do I have to do anything unsavory?"

"Nope."

"Then I ain't interested."

We both laughed.

"Just listen to me for a minute. Here we are in the big state of Colorado with nothing but time on our hands. Just look how beautiful it is with all them trees and mountains." He was starting to sound like a travel commercial on TV. "You know what are in them mountains?"

"Grizzly Bears. Looking for fat juicy groceries just our size."

"No, you fool. Lakes! These mountains are just full of them."

I could tell by the look in Levi's eyes and the excitement in his voice that there was something special about lakes to him, but I'll be damned if I knew what it was.

"Well, I can see you're just plum happy about the fact that there's some fresh water up here. And I'm happy for you, by gum." I slapped him on the back and gave him that look you give someone you know is a little touched in the head. "But I fail to see what that's got to do with money."

"It ain't just the lakes, Hoss. It's what is in the lakes. Them lakes are full of fish. We can catch them and eat them. We'll capture our own groceries and we'll camp out so we won't have to pay for a room. And we won't be in town at all, which means we won't be getting in any bad trouble. You know what happens when we get around civilized people."

I sure couldn't argue with that. Levi's plan was close to brilliant — except for a few little incidentals.

"If you're so smart, Levi, answer me this. Do you like eating fish?"

He hesitated, then set his jaw. "All right, it ain't my favorite, but neither is bologna and I've been eating that stuff every night for the last three weeks."

He had a point. But I wasn't going to let him off easy.

"You ever been fishing before?"

"I went once or twice when I was a kid. How hard can it be? You get a string and put a hook on it. Then you tie it to a stick, slap some bait on it, and poke it in the water. When you pull it out you got a fish."

I hadn't done much fishing myself, but something didn't sound quite right.

"You are talking about fishing poles, aren't you?"

"Yep."

"Where are we gonna get them hooks and stuff like that?"

"Don't worry. We'll fake it if we have to. You ready to head for the high country or not?"

"How high are you planning to go?"

"Two, maybe three hundred feet up. Hell, I don't know, Hoss. You worry too much. We got them two old sleeping bags in the back, a full tank of gas and seventeen dollars. What else does a man need?"

All of a sudden I was feeling prosperous.

"Uncle Earl's got a place just outside of Durango. It's right near one of them lakes up there. I don't remember what the locals call it, because he always called it Stub Toe Lake. Said it had more rocks in it than water."

"And there's fish in it?"

"Yep. And he said I can use it any time I want to. He hardly ever goes up there any more, so I'm sure it'll be empty. We can stay there a week.

"A week?" I was wondering why all of a sudden he wanted to spend an entire week in the outback. "Levi, have you gone and done something illegal you ain't told me about?"

"Nope. I just want to go fishing. We ain't got nothing better to do."

"That's just what we need. A cozy little hideaway. Do you know where it is?'

"Oh, sure. I been there before."

51

We bought a sixpack and a cheap jug from the bootlegger. I let Levi drive because he knew the way. I should have known he'd head right for the back roads. Force of habit, I guess. The good thing about the back roads is they have better scenery, and I got to admit, the scenery in the high country is sure enough purty. The bad thing is them old rocky roads. They are bumpy as hell and he hadn't missed a one. After three hours my bones were starting to rattle.

"Levi, are you sure you know where you're going?"

He took a big swig off his jug and swerved between the trees on one side of the road and a big rock on the other.

"I got a mind like a sh-teel trap! This here is a shortcut."

"A short cut? We're liable to run out of gas on your shortcut. Maybe we're about out now. How much gas we got left?"

I leaned over to take a peek at the instrument panel.

"Damn, Levi. The gas gauge is broken."

He shrugged and took another swig. "Don't need it. I know how far this jalopy will go and we ain't gone far enough yet."

The more he drank the slower he drove, and the slower he drove the wider he swerved. That skinny little road was downright treacherous. The further we went the narrower it got. That beautiful scenery all of a sudden started looking real scary. I popped a top to another beer. Maybe I'd get drunk and then I wouldn't care if I wet my pants.

I didn't have to worry but a minute longer. When Levi swerved to miss the next tree, I spilled half a can on my lap.

"I'll say one thing, Levi. I sure am glad the road crew left all these trees on the sides of road. Long as we can keep bouncing off of them, we'll never get lost."

"You know what's wrong with you, Hoss?"

"Yeah, I know what's wrong with me. I'm too poor to hire a chauffeur."

"Naw. What's really wrong with you is that you got no sense of adventure."

Levi sure knew how to insult a man.

"No sense of adventure? Didn't I go out with that cousin of yours? What was her name? Lippy. Yeah, that was it, Lippy."

"Libby. Her name is Libby. And she's good looking, too. It runs in the family."

"Sure. But that wasn't the adventurous part."

"What are you talking about?"

"You told me she worked at the women's prison, and I thought you meant like a guard or something. You neglected to tell me she was working there because some judge told her she had to. Ain't I right?"

"She was on parole."

"Yeah, I know that now, you idiot. But she had only got out of there eight hours before our date."

"What's so damn adventurous about that?" Levi slurred. "You probably been out with a dozen women that have been in prison."

"No I ain't. Anyway, she told me I was the best looking man she'd seen in quite awhile. I should have known right there that something wasn't right."

"She just asked you to come on over to her place after the dance. What's wrong with that?"

"I'll tell you what's wrong with that. I went over there, and the first thing she did was show me her gun collection. And you got the nerve to say I have no sense of adventure. I'll tell you who has no sense of adventure. Ole Jerry, that's who."

"When you're right, you're right, Hoss. Poor ole Jerry's probably still got lipstick stains on his collar from that ole gal we fixed him up with. She sure was a prize all right."

"Say, you never did tell me what your cousin was in prison for."

"Well, Libby used to be one of them exotic dancers. She wore a cowboy hat and a little gun belt with pistols in the holsters. She had a whole routine worked out to that Conway Twitty song *Desperado Love*. At the end, she'd fire off a couple of rounds of blanks. Anyway, her boyfriend came in one night when he thought Libby wasn't working. He didn't know she was filling in for one of the other girls that got sick. Libby spied him out there playing around with the gal that dressed up like Lil Bo Peep. She was sitting on his lap and the two of them were wrestling around like a couple of teenagers. Boy was he surprised when Libby came riding out on her stick horse. She played it real cool until the end of the song. Then she shot him with real bullets."

"You mean she killed her boyfriend."

"Hell no. Libby's a good ole gal. She just shot him in his vital parts, if you know what I mean."

"Well, ain't that a comfort! I dated your sweet cousin who never kills anybody, just mames them."

Levi pumped the brakes. "Look up ahead there, Hoss. I told you I knew where I was going."

"Looks like a farm. What's so special about that?"

"It is a chicken farm. That's where we're going to get some fishing bait."

"Fishing bait from a chicken farm?"

"That's where Uncle Earl always stopped."

Levi turned into the drive and goosed it. When the dust cleared, I looked out the window. He had stopped an inch from the barn.

"There's Mr. Hedge."

"How do you know his name?"

"I told you I came here with Uncle Earl. I also told you I got a mind like a steel trap. Besides, see that old sign propped up against the water trough over there?"

Sure enough, it said Hedge Chicken Farm.

"You wait here, Hoss. I'll be back in a minute."

Levi stumbled out of the car and went to waving and hollering at Mr. Hedge. When he got his attention, the two of them talked a little bit and then they headed out to a shed near the chicken coops. Levi came back with a rusty can and put it on the floor board in the back. It was a big coffee can. One of them three pounders.

"How much did you have to give for the bait, Levi?"

"Heck, he didn't charge me a dime. He's a nice ole feller. Gave us enough bait for a week."

Levi peeled out on the same road and every time it forked he turned right. After we drove another thirty minutes I noticed something.

"What the heck is that smell?"

"What smell?"

"That rotten smell. Did you . . ."

"Oh, it's probably the bait."

"The bait?" I thought he was kidding. "Levi, I grew up on a farm and I ain't never smelled a worm that stinked."

"Well, there you go. You ain't no fisherman neither. Them ain't worms."

I was half scared to ask. "If it ain't worms, what is it?"

"Man, can't you figure it out?"

"No I cannot figure it out. And I damn sure ain't opening the can to see. But if you don't tell me what's rotting back there, I'm kicking it out."

"Don't get hasty, Hoss. It's just chicken entrails."

"Chicken entrails? How's that supposed to work, genius? Don't tell me the fish are gonna jump in our net to get away from the smell."

"Don't give up your day job, Hoss," Levi grinned. "I can tell it's gonna take awhile for you to become a successful fisherman. First of all, you got to know where to find the fish. That's important. And then you got to . . ."

"Levi, I am not in the mood for a lecture. I just wished you would do something to get rid of that smell."

"I ain't throwing our bait out, Hoss. Them entrails is the best bait you can use."

I just could not imagine anything alive that would be tempted by that stink. I rolled the window down and stuck my head out.

"Look there!"

Levi slammed on the brakes and we stopped at the edge of a slope. At the bottom of it was an itty bitty lake.

"That's it?"

"That's it. Purty, ain't it?"

On the road down was a stand of skinny pine trees, and not ten yards from the lake was Uncle Earl's chalet. We parked next to the trees. From the looks of the place, Uncle Earl hadn't been around for quite some time.

"Home sweet home!" Levi tipped up his jug.

"I thought you said your uncle had a cabin up here."

"I did not!" He got out and staggered to the front of the car. "Come on, Hoss. What's the matter? You got something against trailers?"

"No. I guess I just figured your uncle had better taste is all."

It was one of them little trailers people pull behind their cars when they go on vacation. I popped open another beer and went to have a closer look. Even though I wasn't all that interested, I was sure enough happy to get away from the fishing bait.

That rig was something else. It looked like it had been spit out by a cyclone. About half of the roof was coming off, and it was leaning on an angle because one of the tires was flat. Anything that was wood was almost

56

completely rotted off, and someone had smashed all the windows. The door was gone, too. You could see right inside. It was stuffed full of rags and boxes, whiskey bottles and empty cans, and on top of all that was about six inches of mud and dirt.

"Kind of dilapidated," Levi said.

"No shit! When's the last time your Uncle Earl was out here? Before or after the Civil War? I've seen bigger horse trailers and cleaner outhouses. A snake would have to coil up to make room to lay in there. And speaking of snakes, that thing is probably crawling with them. You know I'm not a fussy man, Levi, but I ain't going in there and that's all there is to it."

"Would you quit your whining. It ain't for sleeping in, it's for storing stuff. We're going to camp out, remember?"

"I ain't no boy scout, you know." I took another swaller and started back to the car. "Hey Levi, I got an idea. Why don't you put the chicken guts in there and I'll stay out here and keep an eye on the booze."

Levi shrugged and walked over to the trailer door. With one foot on the ground he stretched inside to reach a dusty tarp that was underneath an old metal toolbox. He was grunting and a-cussing and just a-wiggling his butt for all he was worth to get that thing out of there. When he gave it one good tug, he fell backwards and that canvas came out of there with enough dirt on it to plant a crop of peanuts.

Sputtering and stumbling, Levi drug it over to the car and dropped it in a heap near the trees. After another pull on his jug he got brave enough to crawl inside and started tossing out trash of all sorts — candy wrappers, an ole army jacket, three girly magazines, and finally — a rope.

"Here, help me tie this to them trees and we'll throw the tarp on top and make us a tent."

57

He idled over to the trees and tried to throw the rope up to one of the limbs that was hanging down over the car.

"I'm a little tipsy, Hoss. Why don't you climb up one of them trees and hang this up there. I'd do it myself but I'm a-scared of heights."

"You big sissy." I growled. "Give me that rope."

While I was tying the rope, Levi gripped the tarp, planted both feet, blinked, squinted, then rared back and threw as hard as he could. For a minute I thought he would get that tarp up there without my help. I don't know why he didn't let go of it.

"Shhhiiit!" he hollered as he cartwheeled down the slope toward the lake.

I started running after him but I went to laughing so hard I couldn't catch up. He got wrapped up tight in the tarp and rolled right out in the lake.

"Help! Help! I'm drowning."

If I had stopped to think for a minute, I would have known it wasn't possible for an ant to drown in that lake. But I was kind of tanked myself and I couldn't let my buddy die.

All I could see was that tarp and a leg sticking out. I was starting to think that the both of us might never get out of there alive. Levi was too tangled up to tread water and I sure enough wasn't no swimmer. I could paddle around enough to keep afloat if I had to, but I sure wasn't no lifeguard.

I waded in after the leg. There was so many rocks on the bottom I couldn't stand upright. I wondered how a fish could swim in that damn pond. When I got to Levi, the water didn't even hit me at the knee. I pulled the tarp off of his face and sat him up.

"Damn, Hoss!" He looked up at me and spit out some mud. "Thanks for saving me."

58

"You knot head. This ain't nothing but a puddle. The only way you could drown is if you tried to drink it."

He looked at the water and back up at me. "It felt a whole lot deeper in the dark."

"Levi, this little adventure of yours is about as much fun as chasing old women. That trailer is a dump, you can't build a tent, and I've spit more water than this lake of yours could ever hold."

"I didn't know you was such a pessimist."

I rolled Levi out of the tarp and we climbed back up the slope.

"Come on, Hoss. Let's finish building this tent. Then I'm gonna get our sleeping bags out. I'm tired."

"That's the best idea I've heard. Only let me sling that tarp this time."

Our tent wasn't half bad. Ole Fred Flintstone would have been proud of us.

I sure was glad we had those sleeping bags. It gets cold as the dickens in the mountains at night, even in the summer. Of course, we had consumed a lot of anti-freeze. If we had caught frostbite or anything like that, we probably wouldn't have noticed it.

The sun was shining right in my eyes the next morning when I rolled over to see if Levi was awake yet. His sleeping bag was empty. I looked around for a sign of any bears. It was mighty quiet up there and I figured I could hear a bear if there was one.

"Leeevi!" I hollered.

When he heard his name echo across the lake, he climbed out of the trailer. He had a rusty old fishing pole in each hand.

"Look here what I found."

He tossed one to me.

"Come on, Hoss. Let's scare us up some breakfast."

59

Fish for breakfast kind of made my stomach turn, but I wasn't discouraged none. I figured by the time we caught one it would be suppertime anyway.

"Where's your famous bait?"

"Right here."

Levi reached down and picked up the coffee can. When he took the lid off that thing I thought I was going to pass out.

"Damn, Levi." I pinched my nose and closed my eyes. "Why don't we just toss that stuff in the lake? The smell will kill every fish in there. They'll just float to the top and we can take our pick."

When I opened my eyes, Levi was making some damn ugly faces himself, and holding that can as far away as his arm would stretch.

"I guess Uncle Earl had a reason for keeping this stuff in that ole cooler of his."

"Yeah, I guess that it'd be it." I shook my head.

Levi muttered something about keeping the bait out of the sun so it wouldn't spoil. He walked over to one of them spindly little trees, put the can down on the ground, then popped the lid off and ran back over to me.

"Well, don't just stand there, Hoss. Put some bait on your hook and let's go."

"You want me to heave up all that beer I drank yesterday?"

"Hell. It ain't so bad. Just take a deep breath, put a hunk on your hook and throw that sucker in the lake."

"I'm not all that hungry yet, Levi. Why don't you show me how it's done?"

He huffed and puffed like that wolf in the fairy tale. Then he sprinted over to the tree, reached in the tin and grabbed a slimy handful, and ran as fast as he could down the slope to the lake. He wadded that junk up on his hook and flung his line into the water.

"See there," he hollered. "That was easy."

I didn't believe a word of it, but what choice did I have? I pulled my shirt up over my nose, walked over to the can, and plucked out a hunk of them stinking guts. I hot-footed it down to the lake, hooked that goop on my line and tossed it in the water.

"How long is this supposed to take?" I asked Levi after I'd stood there awhile. "I've been eyeballing this here string for a good ten minutes and I ain't had a single bite yet."

"Have some patience, Hoss."

He had found himself a forked stick and propped his pole up in it. I decided to just sit there and hold mine. I was afraid if I laid back there like Levi with my hat over my eyes, I'd fall asleep again and some fish would take off with my pole.

An hour later Levi was snoring. His pole hadn't had so much as a tug and neither had mine. I couldn't take it any longer. I waded out into the lake and started beating the water with my pole.

Levi jumped up. "What the hell are you doing? You're gonna scare all the fish away."

"Scare what fish? I ain't seen nothing in this here puddle and neither have you. I got a better chance of clubbing one to death than forcing him to eat that bait of yours."

"Hoss! Get out the lake and quit making so much noise."

"You know patience ain't my strong suit, Levi."

"Yeah. I know that, but I think I'm gonna get a bite any minute now. Why don't you just take a walk and go cool off?"

"Take a walk? You know I hate to walk. I'd chase a horse five miles just so I could ride him."

"Now, that's sure enough cowboy logic. If you could figure a way to fish off horseback, you'd probably spend the rest of your life right here."

"I'm lazy and impatient, Levi. I ain't touched."

Suddenly ole Levi jumped up and grabbed his pole. "I got one! I got one!"

Sure enough he did. It was big enough to make a meal of, too.

"I told you, Hoss. You just got to have patience."

"I don't know why I need any. Seems like you got enough for both of us."

Levi ignored me. "You start a fire, Hoss. I'll clean our lunch right here."

Now, that was one thing I could do. I'd even started a fire a time or two when I didn't mean to. There sure enough was plenty of fuel up there in them mountains and I had me a fire in no time. After the exercise I had even worked up an appetite.

Levi was doing the cooking and complaining about my fire all the while.

"This fire is big enough to cook a moose, Hoss."

"Well, I was hoping maybe one would come along and we could eat him for breakfast. I told you I ain't real fond of fish."

"Why don't you have another beer? And stomp out some of them flames while your at it. You want your breakfast cooked or cremated?

I thought he'd never quit complaining about my fire. But after a couple more beers, we both agreed the fish tasted pretty good.

After lunch we laid down under the tarp for a nap. Everything was working out after all, but by evening I was getting awful bored of nature.

"What are we going to do now, Levi?"

"Well, there's a bar about ten miles up the road."

"No kidding?"

"No kidding. You want to check it out?"

"If you're waiting on me, you're backing up."

We hopped in the car and took off. About halfway there we came to a little gas station.

"Maybe we better gas up now while we have a chance, Levi."

"I'm thirsty. We'll stop on the way back."

I guess I didn't have a whole lot of faith in ole Levi. Even though he had found Uncle Earl's place and caught that fish and all, it wouldn't have surprised me a bit if we had just drove around in circles for an hour or two. In fact, I was expecting to end up back at camp any time, but I'll be damned if he didn't drive right to that watering hole — The Lost Weekend Bar.

The place wasn't too elegant but it sure was popular. When we drove up we might near ran over half the customers. That joint was plum full and five or six of them had spilled out onto a grassy spot out front. Two other fellers were wandering around in circles, and one ole boy was having a hell of an argument with a tree. Except for Levi getting tangled up in the tarp, this was the only entertainment I'd seen since we left home. So I stood there for a minute and watched. That idiot was just a-pounding on that tree. He'd yell for a bit, mutter to himself for awhile, and then he'd get real mad and knock hell out of that poor ole tree. Yep, the place looked like it had some possibilities all right. Trust ole Levi to find a honky tonk clear up in the mountains.

"Levi, you devil you. I know what you're doing. You're trying to corrupt me. You want to ruin my good reputation."

"Damn, Hoss. You found me out."

"What the hell! Lead the way, you wicked man."

"I figured this would be a safe place. There ain't no horses to steal. And no cops to break up the party. I say we have a little fun, get a couple of sixpacks to go, and head back for camp before dark."

I got a real eerie feeling when we walked in. There wasn't one other cowboy in that place. Now, me and Levi had been in some rough bars before, and we had done battle with some ornery ole boys — miners, loggers, and even bikers — but I had never seen such a snarly bunch of men in all my life. Most of them were missing teeth, and it looked like their hair hadn't seen a comb in months.

We each ordered a beer and I found a table at the end of the bar where we could have our backs to the wall. I asked the bartender to bring us two sixpacks to go. He wasn't exactly friendly, but he was more civilized than his customers. Hell, them ole boys even smelled bad. In fact, one smelled worse than Levi's fishing bait.

After my first mouthful of beer I was already thinking it was time to leave when I turned around and saw a female. She was uglier than two of them mountain men put together, and she was headed in our direction.

"Would you look at that Levi? I think that ole gal over there has her eye on you."

"You can have her, Hoss," Levi chuckled. "She's way too purty for me."

When I took another look, my blood turned cold.

"Unless I'm seeing double, pard, I think there's two of them coming for you."

Both of them women had shoulders like a linebacker. One was wearing bib overalls and a tool belt. You could have slung a cat through the gap between her front teeth, and her hair looked like it had been paved with asphalt. The other one's hair was dishwater blonde and real stringy. She had on a pair of them shoes with tall, skinny heels, a red skirt with white patches sewed to it, and earrings to match — them red-and-white bobbers that fishermen use.

The one in the overalls strolled up to Levi and spit a stream of tobacco juice at his feet.

"You know," she said as she squeezed into the chair next to Levi, "I just love cowboys."

I think Levi swallered his chew, which was okay because he sure wasn't going to out-spit that ole gal. He tried to get up and she just snapped him back in his chair like a yo-yo. Yessir. Like it or not, Levi had sure enough found him a girlfriend. He took a big swig out of his bottle. I guess he figured if he couldn't get away, at least he could get drunk. And since he was doing the driving, I decided I might as well join him.

I ordered some more beer and said to his date: "Ole Levi here was just saying how purty he thought your were."

Beer spurted out of Levi's nose and his mouth, and all over his shirt. Them eyes of his was burning holes in me and I knew just what he was thinking. But before he could get a word out, that ole gal snatched him up and planted a lip-lock on him. Hell, she had a half-nelson on him. He couldn't move his head at all, but his feet sure was a-dancing. By the time he managed to pry her off of him, she had built up so much suction that she popped loose like a champagne cork.

"Damn, woman!" Levi sputtered. "Are you trying to suck the life out of me?"

"No, cowboy! You just look like the kissing type. That's all. There's not many of you fellas that come in here."

Levi looked over toward the bar. "Hell there ain't! There's so many fellas in this place, me and my partner just barely found a place to sit down."

"But they ain't cowboys," she whispered kind of low in his ear. "I'd like to keep you around for awhile. My name's Cat. That's short for Caterpillar. What's yours?"

"Caterpillar? You mean like them bugs that turn into butterflies?"

"No, silly. Like tractors. You know. Caterpillar tractors?"

65

Levi looked a might pale. If I hadn't seen Cat's partner coming at me, I probably would have laughed.

"Woof!"

"Woof?" I squeaked.

"That's right cowboy. Woof! Woof!"

Levi laughed. "I get it. She's Cat and your name's Dog, right?"

Dog jumped up in my lap and buried her face in my neck.

"You're friend is a real comedian," she said to me. "My name's Dobie. That's what my friends call me. All my close friends, that is."

I was too scared to asked her what everybody else called her.

She growled and pressed her cold nose against my neck and sniffed.

"Ooooo-wee! This boy wears that fancy smelling stuff, Cat."

Cat spit through her teeth again.

"What's it smell like, Dobie?"

"I can't tell for sure," she sniffed again. "What are you wearing there, cowboy?"

I hadn't had a bath in two days, let alone a shave. There was only one thing she could be smelling.

"It's called Fish Bait."

"Mmm-mm! My favorite!"

"Hey Hoss, you should go fishing more often," Levi snickered. "That's quite a catch you got there."

I swear I could see the toes of my boots curl up when he said that. But that was about all I could see. Dobie had wrapped herself around me and was squeezing so hard my hat fell off.

"Oh no!" she squealed as she reached down to pick it up. "Don't move. I'll get it."

How could I move? She had my left foot pinned to the floor with one of them spiked shoes of hers.

Dobie plopped my hat on her head and went to messing with my hair. I guzzled down another beer and that's when I realized I'd had more alcohol than I needed.

"Say, Cat," Dobie said after she got tired of combing my hair. "Since we finally found us some real men, maybe we ought to go to the Loggerette's room and powder our noses."

"I'm with you, Dobe. Let's go."

Boy, was I glad for a chance to escape. Just as soon as they were inside the bathroom, me and Levi lit out for the back door. We didn't even finish our beers. We made a dash for the car, tossed the sixpacks through the window, dove into the front seat, and sped out the parking lot as fast we could.

Levi reached under the seat for the whiskey and took a couple of pulls.

"Maybe if I'd had enough of this before we went in there, that gal would have been better looking."

"Damn, I don't know what you're complaining about. Did you see the tattoo on the one that was on top of me?"

"No. I didn't see no tattoo. What are you talking about?"

"Come to think of it, I guess you didn't have a real good view from where you was."

"You're right about that," Levi grinned. "That woman pret' near had me smothered."

"That ain't nothing! That Dobie gal had me pinned to the floor with them spiked heels of hers. It was scary."

"Scarier than going on a date with my cousin?"

I had to stop a minute and think about that one.

"Yeah. I don't know if she's got a gun collection or anything like that, but I sure enough wouldn't go to her house to find out."

"Like I said, Hoss, you just ain't got no sense of adventure. She didn't look all that scary to me."

"I haven't got to the real scary part yet, Levi. That didn't happen until she knocked my hat off. When she bent over to pick it up, that's when I saw she had a tattoo."

"Aw, come on, Hoss. Girls don't have tattoos."

"That one does. And if it was any higher up, she'd have to get naked so a feller could read it. It was a vulture and it had big red letters across it that said 'Dead men don't tell'."

"Holy shit! I guess it's lucky we got out of there with our hides."

"This is one hell of a trip you come up with, Levi, but I'll say one thing. Uncle Earl's place is starting to sound awful dang good to me."

"Yeah, me to." Levi looked a little sheepish as the car started to choke. "I think we're out of gas."

We'd been going so fast and jabbering so much, I didn't notice if we'd went by the little gas station or not.

"Levi, I told you to stop on the way to the honky tonk. Damn!"

"Ordinarily I'd argue with you, Hoss, but not now. We got more important things to do."

"What kind of important things do you have in mind, genius? It's getting dark and I think that's storm clouds I see in the east over there."

"Here!" Levi handed me the two sixpacks and reached for the whiskey bottle under the seat. "Better have a hit, Hoss. We're gonna need it till we make it back to camp. You know how cold it gets at night up here."

I never did like walking and I like it even less if it's raining. Levi was dead on about it getting colder. Neither one of us had a jacket and we were soaked to the skin.

"Damn!" I wiped the rain off my face. "The last thing I need today is a cold shower."

I was about ready to pile up some tree branches and make us a shelter when Levi spied a light up ahead in the distance.

"You know, Hoss, we could get there a lot faster if we got off this road and took a shortcut straight to that light."

"Well what are we waiting for?"

It was so dark we couldn't see anything but the light, so we just kept going towards it. We were double-timing when all of a sudden there was a splash.

"Oh shit, Levi! We're in a creek!"

"It can't be very deep. Just grit your teeth and keep going, Hoss."

Now, I really didn't want to get any wetter or colder than I already was, but the alternative wasn't any better, so I kept on a-splashing.

"I would've been better off taking my chances with that Dobie gal than following you out here," I grumbled.

"Damn Hoss, here we are in the middle of no-where, cold and wet and out of gas. You just know our luck's got to change."

"Shut up, Levi," I said under my breath.

All of a sudden the bottom went out from under my feet. I heard a gurgle as my boots filled up but that was all. There was no sign of Levi. I started shivering. It sure enough was cold!

"Wow that's deep!" Levi came up a-sputtering and waving his bottle in the air. "I think I just fell off a ledge."

"No shit!" It was all I could do to keep my head above water. I took one step toward him. "This here is the real lake, Levi. Why didn't you bring the fishing poles and that good bait of yours? The way our luck's running, we probably would have caught a whole bucket of fish in here."

"Save your breath, funny man. You're going to need it."

Levi was right, of course. Swimming with a six-pack in each hand ain't the easiest thing in the world. But the cowboy code says you don't ever give up the booze, so I started paddling in the direction of the light and prayed we wouldn't find no more ledges before we got to the other side. I had heard stories about lakes with no bottoms. Them real deep, cold ones where folks drown and nobody ever finds their bodies.

I sure was glad when I saw Levi get a foothold and pull himself out of the water.

"Hey, Hoss. Hurry up with the beer. I'm thirsty."

He was joking, of course. We were shivering so bad neither one of us could hold a can steady enough to take a drink. In fact, I was shaking so hard I looked like a lawn sprinkler.

"Man, that was cold! We better start moving, Levi. If I stand still very long, you'll have to spray me with WD40 to get my joints unfroze."

There wasn't as many trees on that side of the lake and we could see up ahead for a ways, so we started jogging — well, as good as two ole bull riders can jog. At least it got our blood to circulating.

I was just starting to get the feeling back in my legs when Levi started moaning again.

"Stuck out in the middle of nowhere. Attacked by killer mountain women. Run out of gas and damn near drown'ded. I can't believe . . ."

"I wish to hell you'd shut up, Levi. One thing I don't need is an inventory of our adventures. I was there. Remember?"

I guess you could say our luck was running hot and cold that night. The light we'd been tracking turned out to be a floodlight outside the little gas station, but it was closed. That's when Levi lost it. He walked over to the door and started banging for all he was worth.

"Damn, Levi. Where's that fisherman's patience you're so famous for?'

Levi was so riled up he was cussing and a-kicking like a mad man. Then something exploded. A chunk of that door flew by his head and he passed me like I was hobbled. Dang that ole boy could run! I had to shift into high gear to catch up with him. Just when I came up alongside him . . . Kaboom!

We took off and didn't stop until we were both out of breath. Hell, we ran so hard, and so fast, and so far, that our clothes dried out.

Levi leaned over with his hands on his knees and gasped, "I think we're out of range now, Hoss."

I was blowing hard myself, but I couldn't help laughing.

"What are you laughing at? Four inches to the right and that crazy ole man would have blown my head off."

"I know, I know, but I never seen you run like that before."

"I ought to go back there and teach that old fart a lesson."

"Now hold on, Levi. Just think about it a minute. If you had got woke up from a sound sleep by a drunk that was banging your door off the hinges, what would you do?"

Levi smiled real big.

"I'd blow the sucker away."

It had stopped raining and the moon was high in the sky, so even though we were staggering and stumbling a bit, it wasn't too hard to stay on the road. Lucky for us, we had left our bedrolls back at camp and they had stayed dry under Uncle Earl's ole tarp.

"You know what the good news is?" I said to Levi as I crawled in. "This is a nightmare and I'm going to wake up in the morning and our car is going to be sitting there with a full tank of gas."

"Naw! The good news is the beer's still cold. Want to know what the bad news is?"

"What?"

71

"I don't even want any."

"Me either. Good night, Levi."

The next morning I rolled up my sleeping bag and started to take the tarp down.

"What are you doing to our tent, Hoss?"

"Levi, pack up. We're going to walk to the gas station, get that car started, and then we're going home."

"Home? We only been here two days."

"That's two days too long. I've had all this Daniel Boone stuff I can stand."

"Well, okay, if that's the way you feel about it. Too bad, though. You was just getting the hang of fishing."

"Right!"

I was not looking forward to walking back to the station, but it wasn't near as bad in daylight. In fact, that mountain air was kind of refreshing. I guess we'd walked about two miles before we stopped. That's because Levi had to stop and go in the trees.

"I'll be right back, Hoss."

While I was waiting there on the side of the road I saw a truck headed in our direction.

"Levi, hurry up. There's somebody coming. Maybe we can catch a ride."

That truck was one of them World War II Power Wagons. It had a set of the biggest tires I ever saw and they was spitting gravel every which-a-way, just a-chewing up the road. It had running lights on the cab roof and a pair of elk horns mounted on the hood. There was a coyote's tail swinging from the antenna, too, and it looked like someone had painted it with a broom.

"Where is it?" Levi said as he came running out of the trees.

"Holy shit, Levi! Get back in the there!"

I shoved him and we both ducked for cover.

"What about our ride?"

Levi gave me a look of despair.

"Forget it!"

"But that was a girl behind the wheel. What in the world's got into you, Hoss?"

"There's two girls in that truck, pard. And I'll just bet there's only two gals in the entire state of Colorado that would own a vehicle like that."

We looked around for a better place to hide, but it was no use. Cat had spied us. She brought that truck to a screeching halt and the two of them hopped out.

"They're probably just taking a leak," Cat said as she lit a smoke and dropped the tailgate down. "Let's crack open a beer and wait for them."

I figured if we stayed real quiet they'd get tired of waiting for us, but Levi just couldn't keep his big mouth shut for a minute.

"Look, Hoss." He whispered loud enough so anybody within a mile could hear him. "There's an opening over yonder. Let's go."

"Hey, honey!" Dobie hollered. "I can hear you. Where are you?"

Levi was weakening.

"At least we could ask them to drive us to the station."

"Levi, have you any idea . . ."

"How bad could it be?"

"Well, I don't know how bad it could be for you, but I been sitting here a-thinking. If I had my choice between walking back to Roosevelt County and riding in that he-man truck with those two gals, I would have been long gone before now. The trouble is, you're the one who brung us up here and I don't know which direction is home."

Cat must have heard us talking. She jumped off the tailgate and headed straight for us.

"What in hell are you boys up to?"

73

"If you're playing hide-n-seek, we'd like to play, too," Dobie said.

"Yeah!" Cat yelled. "Coming ready or not!"

Levi started to panic.

"You're right, Hoss. I think we better start walking."

"Not now, idiot. We're staying right here. I'll bet those two can track a flea on a dog."

I watched Dobie polish off her beer and head for a stand of trees that was a good hundred yards from our hiding spot. I sure enough was relieved because I just knew that other ole gal had her heart set on finding Levi, and he was going to need me to rescue him. I pushed some brush aside to see if she was a-coming and then there came a coyote howl from behind me.

"Holy shit!" I hollered. "What was that?"

"Well, would you look what I found." Cat licked her chops and spit a yard of tobacco into the bushes.

"Hey there, young lady," I said, trying my darn'dest to look happy about seeing her. "Where's your partner?"

"She's over there looking for you." Cat grinned that big ole gappy grin of hers, pointed over to Levi, and spit out her wad. "And I been looking for him."

Levi started to make a break for it and that's when Dobie came crashing through the bushes in them wicked shoes of hers.

I grabbed Levi's shirtsleeve. "You're not going anywhere, pard."

"Hey cowboy," Dobie said to me. "How's come you left in such an all fired hurry last night?"

"Oh ... ah ... well, you see, it's like this." My tongue was tied up in knots and I was starting to perspire. "That was because of Levi."

Levi's mouth dropped open. "It wasn't my ..."

"Now, Levi," I said in a real calm voice. "No sense in getting riled up. These girls here will understand."

Levi gave me a blank stare like I was describing a physics equation.

"You see," I continued, "Levi here is just getting over a broken heart."

Both of them looked at him with their eyebrows raised.

"Yeah, I . . ." Levi choked. "Yeah. He's right. I . . ."

"He don't look like the broken-hearted type," said Cat with a suspicious frown.

Dobie reached over to console Levi and he glanced up at her like a little whipped pup.

"Poor thing!" she sympathized.

"Oh no, don't do that!" I pushed her hand away. "It's okay, Levi. Settle down, now."

"What's he gonna do?" asked Cat. "Lick her to death?"

"Not me!" Levi blurted. "I . . . I . . ."

"Don't worry," I said to the girls. "He wouldn't harm a flea. I mean . . . well, his last gal friend took all his money, and . . ."

"Hell," Cat interrupted. "That ain't no problem. I got money, honey, if that's all you need."

I could tell by the look in his eye that Levi was just about ready to stick his foot in his mouth again.

"Uh, well, it wasn't the money part that bothered him so much. It was his dog. You see, she even took his hound. He'd just got him trained, too. Didn't you, buddy?"

Levi finally was starting to act the part.

"Yessir," he sniffled. "That was the best ole hound a man ever had."

"Took his dog?" Cat yelled. "Hell, stealing his money is bad enough, but that's about as low as a woman can get. Did you hear that, Dobe?"

"I sure did. Why, that's downright cruel. Stealing a man's dog can get you killed around these parts."

75

"Yeah, we heard you folks up this way was real fine people," I said before I thought. "Uh . . . that's why I brought Levi up here. We came up to do a little fishing. Get his mind off his dog and all. You know . . . help him forget."

I was positive I had their attention, but I was starting to lose Levi. He was staring up at me like somebody had just hit him upside the head with a rock.

"Now don't feel bad, gals," I continued as I patted Levi's shoulder. "It wasn't you gals' fault. How could you have known that ole hound of his was named Dobie?"

"Dobie?" Cat gave me a puzzled look.

"You mean he named his dog after me?" Dobie squealed.

"Well, not exactly," I said. "But when you gals showed up last night, he had a flashback."

Dobie stared at me kinda stupid like.

"Flashback?"

"Yeah. I guess he had a few too many beers. He went to remembering stuff, and . . . and then he just went a little crazy is all. You can understand that, can't you?"

I stuck my elbow in Levi's ribs. He managed a smile, but I could tell his teeth were clenched. Meanwhile, Dobie and Cat were close to tears. The two of them grabbed ole Levi and squashed his head between their chests.

"Don't you worry none," Cat said. "We got a cousin that raises hounds. She'll give you a new one, and I'll make you forget all about that mean old bitch that ran off with your money."

When Levi pulled loose his eyes were a-bulging.

"Oh, you don't have to go to any trouble for me."

"Hey, I got a great idea," Dobie said. "Since you boys came up here to do some fishing, why don't you let me and Cat take you to our secret hole."

"Yeah. We're the best doggone fishermen you ever met." Cat stuck out her chest. "I'll grab the tackle out of the truck, Dobe. You show the boys where the trail is. We can hike it from here. It's only a half mile or so."

Now, if either of us had really been fisherman, we might have even been real excited about this proposition, but the only thing on our minds was getting away from these two gals, and the faster the better.

"Are you sure we can't make a break for it now?" asked Levi as we started following them down the trail. "It'll be dark again before we know it. And you know what that means."

That got me to thinking again. "Don't get your shirt in a knot, pard. I got a plan."

The gals' fishing whole was real nice — as far as fishing holes go. There was plenty of shade trees to sit under, we had a full cooler of beer, and I even saw a fish jump out of the water. But fishing was the last thing on my mind. I had something up my sleeve and I was just a-waiting for the opportunity to pull it out.

"Here we go boys. All set," Dobie said as she came toward us with two fishing poles and a net.

"Hold it!" I yelled.

Levi froze and both gals stared at me. I definitely had got their attention.

"You know, gals," I smiled, "Me and Levi always fish naked."

Levi was dumbfounded.

"Well, how about that!" shouted Cat. "Did you hear that, Dobe?"

"Holy smoke and jumping Jehovah! These are my kinda boys!"

The gals kicked off their shoes and started dancing around the tree where me and Levi had plopped ourselves down.

"Okay, wise guy, what's next?" Levi whispered to me. "Is it all over, or should I wait around for your encore performance?"

He had a point. I was running out of ideas. "I'm ready to bow out any time, pard."

"Hey, honey," Dobie leaned over and gave me a big ole smooch. "Get out of them ole things and grab a pole. The fish are ready to bite."

"Yeah. C'mon, Levi," Cat hollered. "It's time you forgot about that ole bitch that done you wrong. Let's have us some fun."

"I guess I'm ready," said Levi.

I didn't know whether he meant he was ready to get naked or ready to run. I had to think fast.

"There's only one thing," I said. "Levi and me . . . well, we never get undressed in front of ladies on a first date. So we're going to undress over there in the trees."

"Okay," Cat said. "We'll be waiting."

Levi followed me into the trees and we crouched down behind a big rock, just out of sight of the gals.

"Give me your shirt, Levi."

"That's it! Hoss, you have gone plum off your rocker. I don't even like looking at them ole nags with their clothes on. And it's for sure I don't want them looking at me with mine off. There's no telling what they'll do. No sir! You cannot have my shirt!"

"Damn it, Levi. Quit your whining and give me that shirt. I got a plan. If you want to get out of here, you better start cooperating.'"

"Shit! I'm warning you, Hoss. This better be good."

He handed his shirt over to me and I tossed it out toward the gals.

"Yee haw!" I hollered. "We'll be ready in a minute, girls."

Dobie picked up the shirt and started giggling.

"What else do you cowboys wear?" asked Cat as she undid her overalls. "You got a pair of these?"

When them britches came sailing over the rock, I knew my plan was working. I unbuttoned my shirt and tossed it in their direction. It landed next to Dobie's shoes.

"Oooh. This is fun." Dobie stepped out of her skirt and let it fly. "I ain't never been on a fishing trip like this before."

After the skirt came a petticoat, then Cat's flannel shirt, and a pair of the biggest bloomers I ever saw.

"See there," I said to Levi. "It's working."

"What's working?"

"My plan, you knot head."

"And what are you planning for us to do? Dress up like women? Are they supposed to wear our clothes? What kind of kinky game is this, anyway?"

"Boy, are you dense today! Pick them bloomers up, Levi."

"No!"

"Don't blow it, pard. We're just about ready to haul ass out of here. Now pick them things up before I make you wear them."

I grabbed Dobie's blouse and Levi rustled up the rest of their crap.

"Hurry up!" Cat called out to us. "The fish are really jumping."

"Hang on," Levi called back. "We got a big surprise for you."

I whispered to Levi, "Now you got the spirit!"

"Oooh, we just love surprises, don't we Cat?"

We took off up that trail like jackrabbits and in no time at all we were back to the road. The gals' truck was right there where they had parked it and the tailgate was still down. Levi climbed up on it and peeked into the cab.

"Look, Hoss. They even left the keys."

"This is our lucky day! Hop in. We're getting out of here."

We were silent for about a mile. Guess we were still in shock. Then all of a sudden Levi hollered.

"Yee haw! We made her!"

"Sure did, pard." I laughed. "That was a close call, though."

He looked at me and squinted. "Now we got our freedom, do you suppose we could drive on out to that honky tonk and have a cold one?"

"Man, you sure do like to live dangerous, don't you?"

"No. I'm a might thirsty is all."

"Let me think on it a minute."

The road was starting to look familiar. I figured we were gonna come up on that little gas station, so I told Levi we should stop and get some gas before we did anything else.

"Hell, that ain't no smarter than going to the bar, Hoss. I'll bet there ain't one person up here that don't recognize this truck. What are we going to tell the guy at the station? That we found it abandoned by the side of the road?"

"You're right. We'll tell him that we . . . Let's see . . . Uh . . ."

"Oh shit!" Levi hit the brakes. "I can see it coming already. We're gonna ditch this thing and walk. You already got us in enough trouble for one day, and I . . ."

"Hold it! I got it! We'll tell him some nice ladies asked us to go fishing with them and we ran out of beer."

"That's good. So far."

I could tell Levi still didn't have a whole lot of confidence in me.

"So, we told the girls to relax there by the lake and we'd go get some more. And, by the way, we need some gas for our motor boat, too."

"You gonna tell a bold-faced lie like that?"

"What? That we got a boat?"

"No, you fool. I meant the nice ladies part."

We both chuckled, and Levi said: "That should work. Just as long as he doesn't recognize us from last night."

"It was too dark. He'll never guess it was us."

"I hope you're right."

We drove up to the station real cautious like. Levi stayed just outside by the truck in case we had to make a fast getaway, and I eased up to the counter.

"Howdy, stranger."

Stranger. Boy, was I glad to hear that.

"Howdy, sir."

"Nice looking truck you got there."

"Oh it ain't ours. We met a couple of nice ladies down the road aways where we was fishing. They was nice enough to share their favorite fishing hole with us, so when they ran out of beer, we volunteered to buy some more and they insisted we take their truck."

"Them silly girls. They're always doing that. I keep telling them somebody's gonna steal it someday. They sure do like their beer, too."

Levi poked his head in the door and gave me a scared look.

"Oh, you know Cat and Dobie, do you?"

"Ought to. They're my daughters."

I liked to swallered my tongue.

"Good looking gals. Both of them."

The old man wrinkled his face like he had never thought of that before.

"Well, son, it's hard to tell sometimes. I think they look like a couple of tomboys myself."

"No, not at all," Levi butted in. "Being tough is stylish these days. You know. Women's lib and all that."

"Well, it's my fault, I guess. Lost their momma early, they did. I raised them up best I could."

It was time to change the subject.

"What happened to your door?" I asked.

I heard Levi gulp.

"Some drunken fool tried to beat it in last night," the ole feller said as he patted the double-barrel shotgun leaning against the counter. "He won't soon forget how I chased him out of here, though. Old Bessie here sure puts an end to an argument in a hurry. I think you boys know what I'm talking about."

"Yeah! We sure do," I said.

Levi's eyes were welded to that shotgun. I had to bite my lip to keep from laughing.

"Pretty day for fishing, ain't it?" the ole man smiled.

"Yep. I guess we'd better get back there with some beer before your daughters run dry."

"Don't forget the gas for our boat," Levi reminded me.

Well, there was just one little thing I hadn't thought of. A gas can.

"Say, mister. You wouldn't happen to have a gas can we can borrow, do you? My partner there left ours in the boat and . . . well, if you could loan us one, we'll just leave it with the girls, if that's all right with you."

Considering everything, that ole feller was downright accommodating. We gave him a five dollar bill and told him to keep the change. We put the gas can in the back of the truck and headed for our car. She was right where we left her. That five gallons would be enough to get us back to camp and then to civilization.

Soon as we got back to camp, we rolled up the tarp and stuffed it back in the trailer beside the fish bait. Then we loaded our bedrolls into the car.

"Levi, you drive the car and I'll drive the truck."

"Huh? You ain't really gonna steal their truck, are you? You already got their clothes. Ain't that enough?"

"No, Levi, I ain't gonna steal the truck. Come on, let's go. We got to get those gals' clothes back to them."

"Have you lost your mind? Do you have any idea what they will do to us? Hoss, you don't have a story good enough to get us out of hot water again, and you know it."

"Don't need a story. We'll just go back there, I'll leave their clothes right there in the truck, then I'll jump in with you and we'll be on our way."

"How do you know they'll still be there? I'll bet you they're halfway to their daddy's station already."

"Can you see Cat hiking down the road in nothing but her boots? And can't you see Dobie bouncing along behind her in them stupid high heels of hers?"

"Stop! Why don't you just ask me if I can see my granny naked in the shower?"

"You're thinking of it right now, aren't you?" I chuckled. "You can't help it."

Levi was blushing for the first time since I can't remember when.

"Just look at you, pard. You're red as a tomater."

"I wonder . . ." Levi started muttering to himself.

"Wonder what? Come on, you can tell ole Hoss. I promise I won't say a word."

Levi glared at me. "I was just wondering what it would cost to get a contract out on one worthless rodeo cowboy?"

"You wouldn't do that. You know you love me, Levi."

"I tolerate you."

"Coming from you, that's a compliment."

When I found the gals' fishing hole, I parked the truck and walked back to the car. I could hear Dobie and Cat, and the way they was laughing and a-giggling, I figured they must have already polished off what beer was left in the cooler and didn't care whether we came back again or not.

"They're still down there," I whispered to Levi. "Let's go take a peek."

"Why?"

"Because."

Levi finally had got his fill of horsing around and this time I knew he meant it.

"If you're gonna get tangled up with them ole nags again, you're on your own, buddy." He revved up the engine. "I'm taking off in five seconds. Are you with me?"

I barely got my butt down on the seat before he peeled out, and I damn near fell out because I couldn't get the door closed. We must have been doing sixty down that road before Levi let up on the gas. We came around that curve so fast we damn near ran right through that little gas station. The old man was outside sweeping the drive. He waved and I hollered at Levi to slow down.

"Howdy, mister," I yelled. "We left your gas can with your daughters just like I told you we would. I hope that's okay."

"That's just fine and dandy, boys. Did you catch any yet?"

"Oh yeah, we caught a couple," I grinned. "But we threw them back."

Dressed to Kill

I went to Texas to kill a little time, and to see a buddy of mine that lived on a ranch. It was about forty miles outside of Hobbs. I got there about six o'clock on a Saturday morning. The sun was just coming up and his dad was already loading his pickup with feed. Arnold was sure enough a hard worker. Eddy told me he had been that way all his life.

"Hey Hoss," Eddy hollered when he saw me drive up to the house. "Where did you come from?"

"You know me, Eddy. No telling where I'll show up."

"Yeah, you're just like a bad penny. You had any coffee yet?"

"I can always use coffee."

"My dad will be back in a minute. He'll be glad to see you. Come on in and meet my cousin. Virgil, this here is Hoss."

I had to do a double take when we walked in because I couldn't believe my eyes. I thought I was seeing a real live comic book hero. Sitting at the kitchen table was the silliest looking human being I ever laid eyes on. He was about six-two and weighed a hundred and twenty soaking wet, give or take a pound or two. He had a face like a weasel. His eyes were so close together you could poke him with one finger and hit both of them. His red hair, which was real kinky and more orange than red, stuck out from under the biggest damn hat in Texas.

It resembled one of them sombreros the Mexicans sell to the tourists in Juarez. His kerchief was big, too — big enough to cover the kitchen table — and he was wearing a bright yellow Roy Rogers shirt with white fringe hanging all over it.

I stepped back for a better look. Man, he was a sight! Whoever sold him those high-water pants ought to be ashamed of himself. Them britches were a good six inches too short, and that white plastic belt was stretched thin from holding on to his chrome-plated buckle. That thing was big as a Chevrolet hub cap. I'd bet good money he didn't have that belt on when he bent over to pull his boots on. And them boots . . . well, they was almost as comical looking as the rest of his costume. When he stood up to say hello, I thought he might never come unraveled from that chair. Shaking his hand was a lot like gripping a wet rag.

"Hello, Hoss!" Arnold slapped the dust off his pants before he came in the house. "You're just in time for some coffee."

Arnold was an old time cowboy. Always had a twinkle in his eye like he knew something about you no one else did. He was a powerful looking ole boy, too — tall and slim but tough as a pine knot. His legs were bowed from riding horses all his life and they were twice as long as his upper body, so whenever he was walking towards you, it looked like an egg beater coming for you.

His wife was damn near as tough as him. In that part of the country a woman had two choices. Get tough or die. Alice could ride a horse as good as any man, and she would whip any cowboy that got out of line. She had a soft side, though, and she always acted like she was happy to see me.

"How you doing, Hoss?" Alice smiled as she handed me a cup. "We ain't seen you around here in

86

awhile. Last time I saw you, you was in a dandy of a fight over at the State Line Bar."

The State Line Bar in Hobbs was where the roughnecks from the Oil Patch blew off steam. They were a tough bunch of men all right. I think they liked fighting even more than cowboys.

"Thanks for the coffee, Alice. Yes, ma'am, I'm sure you saw me fighting in that place. But you're going to have to be a little more specific about the time. I ain't never walked into that place I wasn't in a fight."

"It's hard to stay out of a fight in that joint," Arnold grinned. "Hoss, have you met Virgil? "

"Yep."

"He's from Indiana. He come down here to be a cowboy."

"No shit?" I might near bit off my lip trying to keep from laughing. "Well, he certainly is dressed for the part."

Alice looked at me, rolled her eyes, then looked the other way, but Eddy and his dad didn't have the composure that she had. They went to slapping their knees and hee-hawing, and ole Virgil just stood there with a blank look on his face. He didn't have a clue why everybody was laughing, but after awhile he got to chuckling a little. It was like someone who misses the punch line but doesn't want to look stupid. Well, that was enough to get Alice tickled and, except for Virgil, we all got hysterical. You could have heard us plum to Abilene.

Alice wiped her eyes after a bit and asked me if I was going to stay around for a day or two.

"We got a lot of work to do. Sure enough could use an extra hand to help us get caught up."

"Might just as well. I got more time than money."

Arnold finished his coffee and said to Virgil: "Take Hoss with you to feed, son. But keep an eye on him. He's liable to tell you a story and make you forget

87

everything you ever learned in school. I mean this man is full of shit!"

"Don't worry, Uncle Arnold. He can't pull one over on me."

Virgil thought he was real smart. He looked over at me and cackled. Yessir. He cackled just like a hen. It was the dam'dest sound I had ever heard. Come to think of it, he kind of looked like a chicken with that red comb of his. We headed out to the feed truck and that's when I decided to give him a nickname.

Virgil was so cocky, he thought he was running the outfit. He might near knocked me down getting to the driver's seat. Being as how he was family and all, I let it go and climbed in on the passenger's side.

"How long you been here, Pollo?"

"Pollo? What's that?'

"Oh nothing. That's just how you say your name in Spanish."

He grinned real proud like I had bestowed knighthood on him or something.

"Yeah. Pollo. I like that. It sounds better than Virgil."

He turned, eyes forward, ground the truck into low gear, and peeled out of there like he was going to the races.

"Damn Pollo, slow this thing down. You got a date or something?"

That was one of them there rhetorical questions, of course.

"Nope, I just want to get our work done so I can ride Uncle Arnold's horses. You know, the real cowboy stuff. Do you cowboys look after the cows, too?"

"We do everything with cows except wipe their butts."

About then we came on a gate. Now, that ole feed truck was just like any other ole feed truck. The springs were shot and it didn't have brakes worth a spit. Virgil hit them and they went clear to the floor. He froze, and before I could get a word out of my mouth, he had took out that wire gate and parked on top of an old tin bathtub Arnold had put there to water the stock. I looked over at him and he was stiff as a stick. I thought for a minute he had died of fright. Then he blinked those wild green eyes of his.

"You got to pump them brakes, Pollo."

He looked a little sheepish.

"Oh yeah, I forgot. Uncle Arnold told me about that yesterday."

Virgil didn't waste any time getting off that tub. He jammed the truck into reverse and we headed back to what was left of the gate. He sure enough was in a hurry, but every time I reminded him about it he acted like he didn't hear a word I was saying.

"Damn, boy, I told you to slow down."

Virgil pumped the brakes real hard this time and the ole truck rolled to an easy stop.

"That's more like it. Now, let's get to work."

Virgil jumped out of the truck, drew himself up and stuck out his chest.

"I don't have to take orders from you, Mister Hoss. My uncle owns this ranch and I can do anything I want to."

Fence fixing is not something I am overly fond of, and by now I was in no mood to take lip off a greenhorn with no fashion sense. I reached over, grabbed him by the collar and jerked him half off his feet.

"Look, you little butcher knife butt, dim wit. When you cause me to do a lot of extra work because of your ignorance, you will listen. Just be glad it was me and not Arnold that was with you. He'd have whipped your butt for sure."

He started dancing around, and when I let him go he backed away and hollered, "You big brute. I'm going to tell my uncle on you."

"Well, you just go ahead and do that. But you had better duck when you do, because when he finds out you went through that gate and busted up his tub, I guarantee he's going to clean your clock."

He stood there a minute.

"He wouldn't do that, would he?"

"I've been knowing your uncle for ten years. He told you once about those brakes, didn't he?"

"Yeah." He stared down at those stylish boots of his and muttered, "No, twice."

"Well, there you go. He already gave you a second chance. And that was just because you are family. You have done used up all the favors you're going to get from him, Pollo. In this country, you tell a man something once. If he don't get it, then you just figure he ain't paying attention. People round here don't have time for a man who won't pay attention. When I seen you wasn't paying attention, I did something that got your attention."

From the blank expression on Virgil's face, I just knew he didn't have any idea what I was talking about. This boy's education was going to take some doing.

I got some baling wire and pliers out of the back of the truck and went to fixing the gate. If Virgil hadn't been in such a dadblame hurry to go and ride horses, he probably would have just stood there and watched me, but he got bored, and after awhile he offered to give me a hand.

Soon as we got the gate patched up, we headed for the feeding grounds. Arnold had told me there was sixty head up there. But cattle don't stay together. They scatter. So I went to honking the horn to gather them up. You always honk the horn when you feed, so they associate the sound with food. After awhile, you only have to toot a couple of times and they come a-running. Virgil counted until all sixty showed up.

I let Virgil get behind the wheel again and I crawled up on the back of the truck and went to breaking bales and shoving them off the back. This is not a hard chore to do. Providing the driver keeps the truck moving slow and smooth, that is. But Pollo the Conqueror kept stomping on the gas pedal so the truck lurched forward like it had the hiccups. When I fell down the second time, I went to cussing.

"Keep your damn foot off the gas!"

I could hear Virgil cackling.

"Did you hear what I said, you dumbshit?"

All of a sudden he goosed it hard and I cartwheeled off there like a tumbleweed. I landed flat on my back, which didn't hurt too bad, but it did tick me off. I came off the ground just a-cussing. I started throwing rocks and chasing the truck afoot, but that little jerk stayed just out of reach till I ran out of wind. I thought for a minute he was scared of me catching him, but when he saw me all bent over with my hands on my knees and blowing hard, he got out of the truck, stood on the running board, and laughed his fool head off.

"I'm going to put a world of hurt on you, Pollo."

"No you ain't. You got to promise me you ain't going to beat me up, or I'm going to drive off and leave you here."

I glared at him. I knew he was probably just scared enough to do it, so I really didn't have much choice. I gave in.

"Okay, but I drive and you feed."

I knew my chance would come to get even, and my patience paid off. We finally got done feeding and headed back to the house about dinner time. When I walked up the stairs to the porch, Arnold and Eddy were standing there grinning.

"How'd it go, Hoss?" Eddy asked.

"Working with that boy sure enough does try a man's patience," I snarled.

Eddy grinned bigger than ever and Arnold said, "Yep. That's why we sent him with you. We know what a patient man you are, Hoss."

"Very funny, you two. Just you wait! My time is a-coming"

After dinner Eddy, Virgil and me went out to the corrals to work some cattle that Eddy and his dad had gathered earlier. One of the calves had gotten tangled in barbed wire and needed doctoring. Its leg was swollen and infected so we had to give it a shot of penicillin and put some iodine on the open wound. But before we could get at it, we had to separate it from its momma and put her in another pen.

That ole gal sure showed some fight. It took a good five minutes before we got her out of there. But that was the easy part. Teaching Virgil to throw a calf was another matter.

"Come on, Pollo. It's time you learned how to be a real cowboy."

Eddy dropped a loop around the calf's neck and I ran down the rope and showed Virgil how it was done.

"Look here, Pollo. This here is how you flank a calf. First, you got to get hold of the rope with your left hand. Then reach over and get hold of the flank with your right."

"What's a flank?"

I knew this wasn't going to be easy. I pointed to the spot in front of the calf's hind leg.

"That there," I said. "When he jumps, you bring your knee up at the same time."

After I had thrown the calf, I asked him if he thought he could do it without getting killed.

"Yeah, I think so. But I don't want to hurt the baby cow."

"It ain't a baby cow, it's a calf. He weighs four hundred pounds and if you don't do it just like I showed you, that little darling will eat your lunch. Now get over here and take a hold."

Virgil stumbled over next to me and held out his hand. I had no sooner given him the rope, than that calf took off. It jerked him clean off his feet and drug him around the lot twice before it ran over the top of him. Then it circled round and walked over him again and again until it had tore half the fringe off that yellow shirt of his.

Me and Eddy sure was having fun watching the wreck. In fact, we agreed it was about the best show we'd seen in quite awhile.

"Hey Pollo!" I hollered. "Don't let go of that rope."

Eddy was laughing so hard he barely could stand up, but he kept on a-yelling.

"Hang on to him, Virgil. Hang on, boy. You're doing real good!"

That poor dumb kid was taking a helluva beating. The calf didn't give up until it was wore plum out. Then it stopped dead in front of Virgil and stared at him like he had just fell out of the sky and landed there on his butt.

While I ran up and got hold of the calf, Eddy checked his cousin over, just in case he had broke something.

"Damn, Virgil," he said as he bent over and looked him square in the face. "It's a good thing you had your mouth open or you'd have got dirt all over your shirt."

That was no lie. His mouth was plum full. He was spitting and a-blowing, but as hard as he tried to say something, not a word of it made sense. Finally he took a finger and dug out enough mud so he could talk.

"Boy! That baby cow is a whole lot stronger than he looks."

"Yep. Looks can sure fool a man sometimes," I said. "And speaking of looks, I'd say you're going to have to work your wardrobe over a little tonight."

"Yeah. I guess I'm a wreck, huh?"

He damn sure was! That big sombrero was all wadded up and shoved down clear over those big elephant ears of his, and that shirt . . . well, it had taken the brunt of the battle. It definitely was not a working man's shirt. And even if it had been made for show, there was barely enough of it left to tell what kind of show the designer had in mind. Every seam had busted out, the collar was hanging on by a thread, and there wasn't a button in sight. Even the fringe was gone, except for two strings. They was dangling from each shirt pocket so it looked like he had on a pair of them tassels that the strippers in Dallas wear.

Me and Eddy went to giggling like a couple of girls and that was about the time Arnold caught up with us. When he saw Virgil trying to wire the sole back onto one of his boots, he knelt down beside him and rested his big ole hand on the boy's shoulder.

"Damn, son! You look like you've been run over by a freight train. Are you hurt?" Then he turned to Eddy and me. "What's been going on, boys?"

Eddy spoke up first. "He ain't hurt much, dad. It ain't as bad as it looks."

"Yeah. He just got a little bark peeled off is all." I went to shuffling my feet in the dirt. "It'll grow back. Be purty as ever in no time."

"I'm okay, Uncle Arnold." Virgil had got most of the mud out of his mouth, so there was plenty of room to stick his foot in it. "It's only my first time. I did just like Eddy and Hoss told me. I didn't let go of the rope."

The show was over. Arnold's idea of fun, and mine and Eddy's idea of fun . . . well, I guess you could say they was a generation apart. He glared at us and spoke real slow.

"I don't mind you breaking him in, boys. He has to learn. But you had better be teaching him how to do it proper. If that calf had broke a leg, you boys would have been in big trouble. Now get that calf doctored like I told you. And when you're done, you can help me fix fences."

Arnold dusted off his nephew and told him to get in the truck and drive around to the back of the corrals. When Eddy and me walked back there a few minutes later, the two of them were loading fence posts onto the truck. I wasn't real sure if Arnold had got over being mad at me, so when I spied a shiny new aluminum gate propped up between two posts I figured it was as good a time as any to find out.

"That sure enough is a nice gate you got," I said with one of those innocent smiles I save for special occasions and emergencies. "How big is it? Twenty foot?"

"Yep. Got it yesterday." Arnold didn't even look up. He just kept on a-loading poles. "Didn't have time to hang it."

"I guess I could help you hang it." I smiled real big. "If you want me to, that is."

He turned around and went to fussing with some wire. Meanwhile, Virgil had got back in the truck and was driving around the place like a lunatic. When he came to the gate, he got out, took a look at it and shrugged. When he didn't see any way to swing it open, he just pushed it over.

I might near swallered my chew when I saw him get back in that truck.

"Oh Arnold," I said when I heard low gear grab hold. He was still ignoring me so I hollered a little louder. "You had better watch this. I think your nephew is going to . . ."

Arnold turned around just in time to see the back wheels clear the top rail of his new gate. That's when I found out just how mad that ole boy could get. He flat went into a rage. He was cussing Virgil so bad, even Eddy blushed. It was loud, too. Hell, he let out such a squall that the cattle almost stampeded right there in the pen.

I looked over at Virgil who was sitting there in the truck with that orange hairdo peeking out from under his scrunched sombrero. For a minute I almost felt sorry for him. He didn't have a clue what was going on. Oh, he had heard the commotion all right. That's how come he had stopped the truck. But he really did not know he'd done anything wrong. I couldn't say for sure how long it took for him to figure out that his uncle was upset with him, but when he did, his ole face turned white. That truck door flew open and he was out of there quick as a jack rabbit. Hell, he left skid marks in the dirt.

No doubt about it, Virgil was well out of Arnold's reach, and besides, Arnold wasn't one to hold a grudge for long. He had already started to cool off when I saw the truck move. Virgil had left it in neutral.

When that five ton of steel and fence posts rolled back over the gate, Arnold let out a blood-curdling yowl. It was so terrifying that Alice came a-running all the way from the house and passed Virgil who was running in the opposite direction.

"Stop that dumb son-of-a-bitch!" Arnold shouted to his wife.

The roundup had begun. Me and Eddy stood back where we could enjoy it. His maw could really move when she wanted to. Had a set of lungs on her, too. When both her and Arnold went to screaming and chasing, Virgil shifted into high gear. I'll say one thing for Virgil. He might not have been too bright, but he sure enough could run. Those long skinny legs were a-pumping like two pistons. He might have got away, too, if it hadn't been for them damn cheap boots of his. That was his downfall. He had tried mending the bad one with some ole duct tape he found behind the seat of the truck, but it had wore off and that sole was flopping like crazy. When he seen he couldn't get away, he decided to circle around the corrals and take refuge in the truck which had lodged itself atop Arnold's gate. He jumped into the cab and barely got the door locked before Alice come barreling up from the other direction.

"Arnold!" she screeched. "What happened to this gate? Do you know how long it'll take to save up for a new one? Honestly, I don't know what makes you boys tick sometimes. Arnold? Arnold! Where the hell are you?"

In a last ditch attempt to capture Virgil, Arnold had made a detour around the pens and that old egg-beater was coming toward Alice full bore. I thought for a minute he was going to run over her, but he slid to a stop right in front of the gate.

"I'm right here," he barked. "Where's that damn nephew of yours?"

Genius that he was, Virgil had rolled up all the windows and locked both doors. That really got Arnold riled up. He entertained us for another ten minutes or more, although we didn't have any sound effects after awhile because his voice had give out from the first go-around. Still, he was damn good watching. He went to jumping and a-kicking instead of screeching and cussing, and by the time his tantrum was over, he'd knocked big ole dents in all of the old Ford's fenders and the gate looked like it had been flattened by a steamroller.

"Arnold," Alice whined, "What did you go and do that for?"

"It's Virgil's fault. Not mine."

It took a lot longer for Arnold to cool down the second time. He was still mad at suppertime. In fact, he told Virgil to take his plate and go eat out on the porch so he didn't have to look at him.

"Did you see what that knucklehead did?" he asked like nobody had been watching the farm all day.

Eddy choked back a laugh, but I just couldn't pass up the opportunity to get my two cents' worth in.

"Yeah, that wasn't the brightest thing to do. You know something? I don't think Pollo's elevator goes all the way to the top floor."

Arnold looked at me and blinked.

"Pollo? Who in the hell is Pollo?"

"Your nephew," I answered with a grin. "I gave him that handle this morning."

Arnold bit off a piece of biscuit and glared in the direction of the porch.

"Chicken, huh? That damn sure is a good name for that dumb cluck. Especially since I'm gonna wring his neck the next time he pulls a stunt like that."

Alice allowed her husband to rant awhile longer, then she put her hands on her hips and let him have it.

"That's family you're talking about, Arnold. There ain't gonna be any necks wrung around here, and don't you forget it!"

Arnold looked like he'd just been handed a life sentence.

"Did you hear me, Arnold?"

She gave him the look. You know the one I'm talking about — that you-had-better-listen-to-me-or-I'll-make-your-life-miserable-forever look — that mean, down-the-nose glare that a woman gives to her old man when she's heard enough of his bullshit. I had seen that look a good many times myself and I recognized it right off. Apparently, so had Arnold.

"All right, boys," Arnold said to me and Eddy real serious like. "You're just gonna have to remember you're dealing with a greenhorn. I want you to give Pollo . . ."

"Virgil!" Alice corrected him.

"Give him another chance. Now go find him before he gets himself in more trouble."

"I don't know what we'll do with him once we find him," I said.

Eddy smirked. "I could think of a lot of things."

That's when Alice gave me and Eddy the look.

The next morning Arnold told me and Eddy he wanted us to ride the back pasture and check cattle. We were out in the barn saddling the horses when Virgil came strolling through the door. He had on a brand-new outfit. He was wearing another one of them shirts with fringe on it. This one was as orange as a road cone and it clashed something awful with that hair of his. I just couldn't stand it.

"Why are you wearing that get-up?"

"I like this kind of shirt. It's real western looking."

"Western Pennsylvania, maybe," said Eddy.

"Pollo, if you wear that out in the pasture, you'll cause the cattle to stampede."

"Aunt Alice said you're not supposed to call me that any more."

"It don't matter a whole lot what we call you," I said. "If you'll do just exactly what we tell you to do, there's a slim chance you could make a hand. That is providing you don't get killed first."

"Or run out of shirts." Eddy grinned.

The reflection off that shirt had might near blinded me, so I didn't notice his spurs until he started walking and I heard them jingle. Santa's entire team of reindeer don't make that much noise. Them spurs were wicked. I could not imagine who in the world would ever sell them things to a cowboy. Of course, it would be hard to guess that Virgil was a cowboy in the first place.

"You planning on climbing telephone poles?" I asked him. "Or are you fixing to wound one of your uncle's horses? With that set of hooks, I am sure you could do either."

"I don't care what you say. That guy in Woolworths told me these are authentic working cowboy spurs."

"My Dad is going to kick your butt if you stab one of his horses with them damn things. You better take them off."

"I like them and I'm keeping them on. So there!"

"There ain't no place on a ranch for four-inch rowels," I yelled. "Them damn things are meant for Halloween parties."

"I don't care what you say. I'm not taking them off."

"Okay, Pollo. You go right ahead," I grinned. "But I sure as hell wouldn't squat if I was you."

Virgil tripped a half a dozen times before he made it to the tack room. Meanwhile, Eddy took Ole Pete, his Mom's horse, and tied him up while we waited for Jingle Bells to wrap a new piece of duct tape around his boot.

"Why didn't you buy some blue suede boots to match that shirt?" I asked Virgil.

For a minute I thought Eddy might wet his pants.

"Shit, Hoss. You better knock it off or my Mom's gonna get real mad."

I never did like to give up when I was having fun, but I knew I would probably be hungry about dinner time, and as long as Alice was doing the cooking, I figured I had better not do anything to get her upset.

Eddy started showing Virgil how to saddle and bridle Ole Pete. Pete was almost twenty-five years old. He knew he was dealing with a greenhorn, and he still could be an ornery cuss at times. Alice was about the only one who rode him any more. She sure was attached to that old buckskin. I was surprised when she told Virgil he could ride him.

When Virgil reached up to put the bridle on, Pete held his head up as high as he possibly could. Eddy tried to help, but Virgil wanted to do it himself.

"Your dad said he had to learn," I reminded Eddy. "So let him learn."

Eddy came and stood next to me and the two of us watched. Virgil tried every which way to get that thing over Pete's ears. When he got up on the fence, Ole Pete stretched out to the end of his rope so he was just out of Virgil's reach.

"Hey Eddy," I spoke up when Virgil went to climbing the fence for the second time. "At this rate it'll be sundown before he gets him saddled."

Eddy just grinned. I knew what he was thinking. That boy was good watching, and so long as we was teaching him how to be a hand, there wasn't no sense in hurrying to get them cattle counted.

"Here, try this," Eddy said to Virgil as he handed him Arnold's old roping saddle.

That saddle was hell for stout and so heavy it'd make your butt pucker every time you tried to lift it. Virgil couldn't get it above his waist, but he wouldn't let us help him either. So we just sat on a bale of hay and watched. He grunted and groaned for the first four or five tries, then he took three deep breaths, set his jaw, and gave it all he was worth. He almost had it up there when those stupid spurs of his got twisted up in each other and caused him to lose his balance.

"Come on, Pollo," I cheered him on. "You can do it."

It took a minute or two for him to get his spurs untangled, but he wasn't about to give up, and he sure enough didn't want our help. This time he rolled a bale of hay up next to Pete and hoisted the saddle on top of it. Then he got another bale for himself. I figured Ole Pete was getting tired of listening to all that huffing and puffing because he stood there like a statue so Virgil could finish the job and cinch him up.

"There!" Virgil stood up on his bale with a proud look on his face. "I did it!"

"You did a right good job," Eddy said. "Except for one thing. You got to put the saddle blanket on before the saddle."

"What? You mean I got to pull that heavy thing off and start over?"

"That's right." Eddy handed him the pad.

"I'm not going to do it. I'll ride him like this."

"No you will not! My Mom doesn't let anybody ride her horse without a saddle blanket."

Virgil was mad. He hopped down and undid the cinch, then jumped back up on his bale and tugged at that saddle for all he was worth. It's surprising what a man can do when his adrenaline starts to pumping. That saddle slipped off Ole Pete's back like it was a feather. Trouble was, Virgil didn't realize he was top heavy, so when them spurs crossed again he fell backwards and the saddle came down on top of him.

"Shit!" exclaimed Eddy when he heard Virgil gasping for air. "I think he's out cold. We had better go get Dad."

"Oh hell! Let's just leave him here. He's only got the wind knocked out of him. He'll be okay after awhile. If we don't get cracking, we ain't never going to get them cattle taken care of."

About that time, Virgil came back to life and Eddy leaned over him and said: "I'm breaking a cowboy rule here, but I'm gonna ask you one more time to let me saddle that horse so we can get going."

Virgil didn't have enough air in him yet to object. And he didn't have enough strength to push that saddle off his chest either, so Eddy threw a saddle blanket on Pete and did it for him.

I'd just as soon left that stubborn jackass lie there, but my better judgment told me not to. I pulled Virgil up and dusted him off, and the three of us mounted our horses and headed for the pasture.

Virgil was giving us the silent treatment. It was obvious that he didn't appreciate me and Eddy teaching him how to ride a horse, any more than he liked us telling him how to saddle one. Come to think of it, he didn't like nobody telling him nothing. Now, if there is one thing I can't stand, it's a man that is ungrateful when somebody does him a favor. I leaned over to Eddy and waved my rope.

"I'll bet we can get Virgil to predict the weather," I whispered.

Eddy knew exactly what I was thinking. He grabbed the other end of my rope and we rode up behind Ole Pete, him on one side and me on the other.

One of the fastest ways I know to get a horse to buck is to run a rope up under his tail. Of course, Pete immediately took exception to the invasion of his privacy, so to speak. He ducked his head and went to kicking for all he was worth. It really was a wasted effort, though, because Virgil had dismounted on the second jump. He sailed through the air like a Frisbee and landed with a thud. When he saw Ole Pete heading in his direction he started to roll, which was smart for Virgil. In fact, it would have been real smart if he hadn't been wearing them he-man spurs.

"Yeee-ooow!" he howled when he bounced up against a rock.

I swear, I never seen a man shed a pair of spurs that fast. He stood up and cussed — well, if you consider "dadgum" cussing — and then he threw them things so hard he damn near pulled his arm our of its socket.

"Those spurs are worthless!" he muttered.

Now, I'm a man that hates to say I told you so. So I didn't. Instead, I rode up to Virgil and asked: "Did you remember to check for rain while you were up there, Pollo?"

Virgil looked stunned.

"What?"

"I said . . . while you were up there flying around in the clouds, did you see if they had any rain in them?"

He still didn't get it.

"Shit, Virgil!" Eddy spurred his horse in disgust. "You are something else! We got to catch up with Pete. You had better start back to the house. And don't forget to tell my dad why we're not with you."

It was near one o'clock by the time me and Eddy got back to the house. We found Arnold in the living room, relaxing in his recliner, and Virgil was sitting at the foot of the stairs on his suitcase.

"Alice left you boys some dinner on the stove," said Arnold as he got out of his chair and followed us into the kitchen.

"Looks like my cousin decided to call her quits," Eddy said.

Arnold chuckled.

"He didn't get a chance to call her quits. Your mom sent him packing."

"Mom did?" Eddy sounded surprised. "What for?"

"Well, it didn't take much. Virgil went to cussing her horse. Said he was a stupid beast and she ought to send him off to the glue factory. He went on and on about Pete's nasty disposition. Just kept it up until she finally had had enough of his bullshit. That's when she let him have it."

"Damn she must have been mad," I said.

"Mad as I ever seen her," Arnold continued. "She just went nuts. I thought I was gonna have to restrain her. Anyway, she told him, if you can't even get along with Pete, there's no hope for you."

"Where's mom now?"

"She's gassing up the truck so she can drive him to the bus depot."

I was already thinking about how bored I was going to be without Pollo to pick on.

"You mean she won't even let him spend the night?"

"Nope." Arnold looked a little sad, too. "You know something? It really ain't Virgil's fault. His paw never taught him nothing."

"Hell, dad, I don't think none of them folks up there in Indiana ever rode a horse in their life."

"I don't doubt that," I said. "I sure hope they ain't counting on Virgil to teach them when he gets home."

Arnold looked over at Virgil and shook his head. He poured himself a second cup of coffee and told us to sit down and eat.

"Well, now that you boys don't have to keep an eye on that store-bought cowboy any more, you'll have plenty of time on your hands. You'll have them horses all shod by sundown, won't you?"

Room at the Inn

After the Albuquerque show in the fall of 1962 I decided to head over to the rodeo in Roswell. I had had a run of bad luck and I needed one more good ride before I went home. Providing I still had a home to go home to, that is. The days are nice and cool in Roswell that time of year, but it can get colder than a banker's heart at night. Just thinking about sleeping in my old Plymouth made me shiver.

I drove slowly down the main street, keeping my eye out for one of them flea-bag motels that went for five bucks a night. There was two of them. One right across the street from the other. I pulled up to the curb, trying to decide which one looked the best, and reached in my pocket and counted the dollar bills that were wadded up in a little ball. I could afford the motel all right, but then I wouldn't have enough left over for entry fees. Like I said, I just needed one more good ride.

I sure was glad to see my buddy Clint when I got to the rodeo. Whenever I rode in Roswell, I always had ole Clint pull my rope. He was the best. He was a good bull rider, too. But the world would never know how good because he hated to travel. You had to hold a gun on him to get him to drive out past the city limits. It was like he was scared somebody would steal the whole town if he ever left it. Clint didn't like things to be too complicated. I think that's why he was still living there in town with his folks. It was a whole lot easier than packing up his junk and finding a place of his own. He wasn't lazy. He just liked to take life nice and easy. And when things didn't go his way, well he could be one hell of a whiner. Most of the other cowboys wouldn't put up with his belly-aching, but I did.

"Hey Hoss! How's the world treating you?" He slapped me on the back. "How did you do in Albuquerque?"

"Not too bad. I rode one, bucked off my last. But I won part of a go-round. I guess you could say I did a whole lot better than some fool who won't hardly leave his desert palace in this here paradise they call downtown Roswell."

"Still mister funny guy I see. Well, at least I eat regular. And I don't have to sleep in my car. Or fifteen to a room, like the rest of you heathens."

"That just ain't true, Clint. Why, just last month I stayed in a room and there wasn't but six of us."

"Was that all?"

"And one dogger's horse."

"A horse? No shit?"

"Yessir. And you know something? It would have been downright elegant if the horse had been house-broke."

We both laughed.

"So, where you staying this weekend, Hoss? The Roswell Hilton?"

"Well, you got me there. I got just enough of my winnings left to pay my entry fees and that's all."

"I hate to say I told you so, but . . ."

"Right! I don't want to hear it."

"I was just going to say . . ."

"If you can't say something nice, don't . . ."

"Quit horning in on me, Hoss. I am trying to do you a favor."

That shut me up. I was in no position to turn down a favor, even though I knew I would have to repay him some day.

"What's the favor, pard?"

"What I was trying to say is, you're welcome to come and stay at my folks' place if you need to."

"I don't need to do that. I said me a little prayer this morning."

"Yeah. I heard you praying while I was planning my trip to the moon."

"A man's got to have a little faith now and then, Clint. You never can tell. I might just find me a little gal with a room of her own. One that's just looking for a handsome and debonair feller like myself."

"You'll probably find one," Clint chuckled. "I don't know anybody that can come up with a sob-story like you can. You get more pity dates than anybody I know."

"Pity dates hell! I could have just about any woman I wanted in this here town and you know it!"

Clint gave me a weird look and I knew just what he wasn't thinking. There really wasn't that many gals in Roswell that either one of us would want to room with.

"Well, if it doesn't work out, you know you're welcome at my place."

Clint started dragging his gear out of his war bag. The bull riding was going to begin in about ten minutes and he had drawed the first one. I wasn't up until the following night but I decided to hang around and watch him ride.

"You got somebody to pull your rope?" I asked.

"Nope. I was counting on you."

"Sure enough, pard. Who you got drawed?"

"Typhoon. You know anything about him?"

Now, if I was a true friend I would not have told him how bad ole Typhoon really was. After all, Clint was fixing to find out soon enough for himself. But I was still thinking about that comment he had made about me and pity dates. That kind of insult can really get to a man's ego sometimes. So, I decided to tell him everything.

"Holy shit, pard!" I held my breath so my face'd turn white. "I drawed him in Odessa this year."

"Damn Hoss. You look like you just seen a ghost. What's got into you?"

"I don't think you want to hear about that bull, Clint."

"You can tell me, Hoss."

He was starting to sound like an old lady when she wants to get the truth out of you. I knew I had his attention.

"He weighs close to a ton," I said real excited like. "He'll jerk your arm clean out of the socket and send you flying. You had better hit the ground running, because that ox will hook you and everything else that gets in his way."

All of that was true. I was going to make up a few more gruesome details, but I seen ole Clint's eyes already had started getting big. He put his chaps on and went to squatting and stretching, so I changed the subject.

"Say Clint, where do you want to go dancing to-night? How about the Stardust? Isn't that where most of the buckle bunnies go? After you cover Typhoon I'll bet you can walk in there and have any one of them little fillies that you want."

Clint's eyes lit up. "Now that sounds like a plan to me."

About then they started loading the bulls. Typhoon was in the lead. That beast's horns was so long he had to turn his head sideways because he couldn't go straight down the chutes without hanging up. They got him as far as the front chute and tried to shove him in, but he was so big he didn't fit. Those boys tried every which-a-way they knew to get him in there. Finally they hit him with a hot shot. Typhoon jumped forward — about three inches is all — just enough so they could close the gate. He filled the whole chute.

"There's your date," I said to Clint.

"Damn! Would you look at him? It's gonna be fun trying to get down on him the way he's all wadded up in there. How's a man supposed to get his legs down? There ain't even room to spit in there."

I nodded in agreement.

"If I get my legs down and he moves even an inch he'll mash the hell out of them."

I nodded again.

"Damn it, Hoss! Would you quit agreeing with me."

"Clint, when you're right, you're right. Now, stop your bitching. You're starting to sound like an old woman."

"Just look at that set of racks, Hoss." Clint rubbed some rosin on his glove. "Hell, them are antlers. I'll bet his momma was a moose!"

When he screwed up his face and went to looking real ugly, I just had to say something.

"You ain't so purty yourself, Festus. Keep on looking like that and there ain't a gal in Roswell will give you a second look at the dance tonight."

"Hoss, you got to admit it. Ain't them the biggest damn horns you ever saw on a bull? Look at them. They're sticking out on both sides of the chute."

"So what do you want me to do about it?"

"Shit!" He put some more rosin on his glove. "That thing could reach back with either one of them things and drag me off. Or whack me in the grinners if I get tipped forward too far."

"I never heard anyone complain about so many things at the same time. If you want me to, I'll tie a couple of pillows on his horns so he can't mess up that pretty face of yours."

Clint stared down hard at Typhoon and started muttering to himself.

"I don't need no pillows. But I'd settle for a saw. Trim them things down about two foot on each side. That ought to take care of it. Hell, I'd be a hero with the other cowboys if I did that."

"Oh yeah. You'd be a hero with the cowboys all right. But that ole stock contractor would whip your ass."

It's a fact. From a stock contractor's point of view, bull riders are a dime a dozen. But good cowboy-hooking, man-eating, crowd-pleasing bulls, are hard to find, and Clint knew it.

"Thank s a lot, Hoss. I feel a whole lot better now."

When I saw his jaw muscle twitch I knew I had him.

"I'm feeling generous," I said. "So I'm going to give you a little free advice. What he'll do is, he'll go out aways and circle back to the right. So, be ready for him."

"Okay, I've got it. Out and circle back to the right."

"Of course, even if you do get him covered, you know you can't win."

"Huh? What are you talking about?"

"He ain't showy enough."

"You mean to tell me I can't win on that monster? Damn! I don't mind taking a chance on a hooking bull if I at least have a shot at the money. Why should I even get on him?"

"For the crowd, Clint." I pulled my hat down over my eyes, trying hard not to laugh. "Hell, if you don't ride him, at least hang up and give the crowd a thrill."

"Gee. Thanks, Hoss. Just what I always wanted to do."

"Hey, you deserved that one, ole buddy. The last time I hung up, you were sitting up there on the back of the chutes cheering for the bull."

Clint shrugged and slowly climbed into the chute with Typhoon. I waited for him to get his legs worked down on each side, then I pulled his rope.

"Now, get your mind right, pard."

Clint shook his face and Typhoon blew that gate open the minute he heard it unlatch. He made three or four quick jumps to the left, but Clint was still with him.

"Throw a knee in him!" I hollered.

Three more jumps and it was all over. Typhoon launched ole Clint out over his head. It was a one-point landing. His nose was the first thing to touch the ground and it plowed a trench clear across the arena. He was on his hands and knees in a heartbeat, though. He started throwing dirt in ole Typhoon's face, and for a minute I thought there was a good chance that bull might choke to death on the dust. But Clint had not planned his escape route. He was just getting his feet under him when Typhoon came charging up behind him and nudged his butt. Fortunately he was headed toward the bucking chute and his second landing stirred up a bigger dust cloud than the first. Turning cartwheels across the arena with Typhoon on his tail, Clint aimed for the chutes and jumped up and over like a cat.

"Hey buddy!" I hollered when he slammed up against the back of the chute. "You damn near knocked me off my perch."

Ole Clint's face was so dirty, all you could see was the whites of his eyes. He didn't have a lot to say either, on account of he had eaten half the dirt in the arena.

"Damn Clint! That's the best entertainment I've had in a long time. You ought to be in one of them drag races."

Clint was still spitting up dirt.

"So glad I could cheer you up, smart ass!"

"Now Clint, don't be that-a-way. You know as well as I do. It's our sworn duty to entertain the public. It's just too bad Typhoon's flank strap came off."

"The hell it did!" he sputtered.

"Sure enough. The judges are giving you a reride."

The look on Clint's face was almost more than I could stand. I had a hard time to keep from cracking up, but I kept pouring it on.

"You are something else! I think the reason they want to see you ride again is that they liked your little acrobatics so much. Besides, a lot of folks missed your show because they was at the concession stand getting popcorn and stuff. They'd like to have a chance to see it again. Come to think of it, I wouldn't mind seeing that one-point landing one more time myself. It don't hurt a man to learn new stunts from a cowboy that rides so graceful as you do. You are a pleasure to behold."

I couldn't tell who Clint wanted to choke more — the judges for giving him a reride, or me for telling him he had one coming. I went to laughing so hard I swallered my chew.

"To hell with that!" Clint hollered. "I ain't getting on that man-eating son-of-a-bitch again for nothing. I just barely got away with my life this time. Where's them damn judges, anyway? I'm going to kill at least one of them. Damn! Where's my hat? What do they think I want to do? Commit suicide? Try to make me get on that head-hunter again."

"That's right Clint," I snickered. "Give 'em hell!"

It had been awhile since I'd seen Clint so shook up. He really raised the devil with them judges. Meanwhile, all the cowboys were standing behind the chutes waiting to see what was going to happen next.

One of the judges was an old cowboy that had been around rodeos for thirty years or more. Me and Bill got along real good. He was a character, and had a good sense of humor, too. He recognized me soon as he heard me laughing, and figured out real quick what was going on between me and Clint.

Bill waited for Clint to draw a breath before he interrupted him.

113

"Son, you sure are spending a lot of energy for nothing. We didn't give you a reride. I don't think you could repeat that performance even if we did. If I was you, though, I would keep a closer eye on ole Hoss, there. That boy will get you into a whole lot trouble if you're not careful."

Clint had been had good and he knew it. He picked his hat up off the ground where he had thrown it and turned around real slow. He glanced over to the other cowboys, then he looked me straight in the eye and said: "You son-of-a-bitch! Your day will come."

"Sure, sure," I smiled back at him. "You ready for the dance?"

Clint suddenly looked like somebody had hit him with a hammer. You could almost see the light come on behind those wide eyes of his.

"Hell, no! My legs are so weak I'll be lucky to climb in the truck and go home."

"Suit yourself. I'm headed to the dance."

"Say, Hoss," he said real friendly like, "If you don't get a better offer, you're still welcome to come and stay at the folks' place you know."

I wasn't expecting that.

"You mean you ain't mad at me?"

"I don't hold no grudges. You know that. Just one thing. You got to promise you won't wake anyone up. You know my old man gets a little hot if his sleep gets disturbed."

That was true. In fact, his dad was somewhat of a legend in Roswell. Waking that man up at any hour of the day could be downright unhealthy.

I had met Clint's folks a time or two. Nice people. His mother was always a-fussing about us boys not eating right and never getting enough sleep. She worried about all the little things that mothers are supposed to worry about. But his dad was a lot like Clint — always

114

carrying on about something or the other. And when Clint would bring one of us cowboys home with him, he'd mumble and grumble louder than ever. I guess you could say cowboys was his favorite topic when it came to the complaint department. He thought we wasted too much time running from one rodeo to another. We spent way too much money on booze and tobacco, too. There was no sense arguing with him. After all, he was in the majority in them days. Wasn't too many people that had a very high opinion of rodeo cowboys in the sixties.

I got to wondering if I was in the mood for listening to Clint's old man or not. I liked the offer all right, but as cold as it was outside, my car did have one advantage. Peace and quiet.

"Maybe I had better not come to your place," I said to Clint. "There's no telling what time the dance will be over, and you how I am. Hell, I can party all night long. Providing I find the right partner."

"It don't matter how late it is, Hoss. I can't let you sleep in that old car of yours. It probably don't have a heater that works, and a man could freeze to death in this weather."

"How did you know about my heater?"

"Has any of your cars ever had a heater that works? Except in the summer when you don't need it, I mean."

He was right on both accounts. After further consideration, Clint's offer was starting to sound good.

"I will do my best not to wake your dad. You got any more rules I should know about?"

"Well, if you come in real late and all the lights are off, be sure to come in the front door. Go down the hall about three paces. The first door on the left is my room. Got it?"

"First door on the left." I repeated it so I wouldn't forget. "Thanks, pard. I'll be there sometime before sunrise. Don't wait up for me."

"Don't worry. I'll be crashed and burned by then."

The pickings were slim at the Stardust. I don't think I danced more than five or six dances that night, and most of them was with the same girl. Now, I take my dancing seriously, but I hate to have to work at it. Nancy sure wasn't no Miss America, but of all the gals in that place, she was the only one that could keep a beat. She was friendly enough, but dancing with the same woman all night long can get monotonous, especially if she's old enough to be your mother.

When it came time to discussing the after-hours arrangements, I suddenly remembered that I hadn't laid down in two days. Damn I was tired! In my mind, all I could see was Nancy tucking me in bed, patting my head like I was a stray dog, and telling me nighty-night. That about finished off any romantic notions I might have had early on in the evening, so I called it a night and headed for Clint's house.

I had no trouble finding my way. There was a full moon and it was real bright outside. I was glad to see Clint's pickup parked in the drive. I wasn't scared or nothing. I just felt better about busting in with him already there. That's all.

Since the muffler was falling off that old Plymouth, I decided to leave it out in the road. There was no sense making any more noise than I had to. I walked up the drive, tiptoed up the front steps and eased the door open. Even with the full moon shining on the porch, it was pitch black inside the house. I guessed Clint's old man kept all the blinds drawn so the moonbeams wouldn't disturb his sleep. I made my way along the hallway, leaning against the wall and stepping quiet as I could. One, two, three paces. I was doing pretty good. I found the first door on the left and opened it. Thank goodness! Clint had left his shade up. At least I could see my way across the room. I even could see him lumped up there under the comforter.

I crept over to the bed, sat down on the edge real easy like and proceeded to pull my boots off. I unbuttoned my shirt and hung it over the back of the chair, and just as I got one leg out of my pants, Clint rolled over to my side and let out a snort. I reached over and slapped him on the butt.

"Scoot over and give me some room," I whispered.

He sat up with his back to me and that's when the hair on my neck stood up like a prickle bush. Now, I had heard stories about spooky things happening during a full moon, but except for Halloween, this was the first time I had ever seen a werewolf. He had a full head of hair that hung down past his shoulders, and he smelled like somebody had doused him with a bottle of dime-store perfume. But that wasn't the scary part. When I took a second look, I seen he was wearing a nightgown!

I plum forgot I had promised to be quiet.

"What the hell are doing in that get-up?" I yelled.

He started screaming in a real shrill voice, grabbed a magazine off the nightstand and went to slapping me upside the head. Then I heard Clint's dad yelling from the bedroom next door.

"What the hell are you doing in there, Grandma?"

I heard my heart drop to the pit of my stomach. Did he say Grandma?

"Owen!" She screamed and hit me with her shoe. "Owen, come quick. There's a man in my room."

What could I do? I grabbed my clothes and made a break for it. Unfortunately, the door was half open and I ran slapdab into the end of it. Talk about crossing your eyes. I bounced off that piece of oak and fell flat on my butt. I couldn't see that moon any longer, but I was sure seeing plenty of stars. And I was hearing some god-awful howling, too. It took a minute for me to figure out that the werewolf was actually Clint's grandmother.

"Oh my word," she whimpered. "He doesn't have any pants on. Owen, can you hear me? He doesn't have any pants on for godsake!"

I wished she hadn't said that. Them's dangerous words in any man's language, and I knew Owen just enough to know that he would shoot first and ask questions later. I jumped to my feet, grabbed my hat and made another dash for freedom. Compared to the bedroom, it was black as a pit in the hallway. I couldn't remember which way I was supposed to turn. First I went left, then I went right, and because I had only one pant leg pulled up, I tripped over the other one and went down again like a sack of feed. Whatever it was I hit on the way down might near knocked the wind out of me, but I couldn't give up. I had to get out of there or die. I kept scrambling and gasping for air.

"Help!" Grandma shrieked. "He's breathing awful heavy. Owen, where are you?"

I had a pretty good idea where Owen was. I could hear someone moving around in the back of house, which was where he kept his shotgun. I raised up and went to scooting towards the front door on my hands and knees. The time for leaving was now!

I struggled to my feet, pulled my pants up, and just as I got hold of the door knob a light came on in back of the house. I could hear Clint's dad stomping down the hall behind me. Then I heard a sound that turned my blood cold. He jacked a shell into the shotgun and suddenly I pictured myself as a bale of hay with a big ole target pinned to it. I jerked the door open and didn't even bother trying to find the latch to the screen door. I just tore right through it like I was Superman. You would have thought I was running in a midnight marathon the way I flew down that drive. I danced across that gravel like I didn't feel a thing.

When I got to Clint's pickup I stopped to catch my breath. Damn my feet hurt! In spite of all the excitement, I had managed to hold on to one boot, although I wondered what good it would do me with my foot all cut and swolled up. My hat was in my other hand, so I put it on instead. I figured I could make it to my car as long as I didn't have to walk over any more rocks, so I stepped out from behind the truck and started tiptoeing across the grass. Then Owen turned the porch light on. I dove head first into the bushes and I guess you know what happened to my hat. I made about as purty a one-point landing as Clint had made at the rodeo, and I had me a good audience, too. Owen was standing on the porch in his long underwear with his shotgun at the ready, and Clint's mom and Grandma were hiding behind him.

Owen peered in my direction like he was just a-wishing to find someone to shoot at. With that big ole moon shining down on everything, he was sure to see something move, and I was a-hoping it wouldn't be me. I held real still and tried not to breathe.

"Owen, are you sure there's someone out there?" Clint's mother asked.

"You think I'm lying?" Grandma squealed. "He's out there all right. I'd recognize him in a minute. He don't have a stitch on."

Clint's dad examined the screen door and peered out again like he was scanning a battlefield. I had caught my breath finally, and I was just going to make my next move when I felt a hand on my shoulder. I damn near wet my pants.

"Looking for me, Hoss?"

I didn't know whether to kiss him or kill him. Then it dawned on me.

"You son-of-a-bitch. You set me up."

Clint laughed and I heard his dad cock the gun. Again.

"Who the hell is out there?" Owen yelled.

"Don't shoot, Pa! It's me and Dan."

We came out of the bushes with our hands in the air.

"What the hell are you boys doing?"

"It was just a joke, Pa."

"A joke? I ought to shoot you anyway."

He lifted that thing up and all I could see was the inside of the barrel. I froze.

"Pa!" Clint whined. "We weren't doing no harm. Please put that thing . . ."

Clint's Mom pushed the gun barrel down.

"Come on, Pa. Leave them boys alone. Let's go back to bed."

Clint started walking slowly toward the house and I followed. I could see Grandma shuffling around up there on the porch, just a-waiting to get a closer look at the man with no clothes on. She leaned over and squinted at me when I started up the stairs.

"Are you the one that was in my bed?"

"Yes ma'am. I'm sorry. I didn't know that was your room. I am real sorry. I didn't have no place to stay tonight and Clint told me it was okay to come here."

"You poor thing!"

Clint's dad snorted and cleared his throat.

"Owen, put that gun down!" She smiled at me and patted my head like I was a lost pup. "You can't shoot a good-looking kid like this. Go on in the house now."

Owen did as he was told and Clint's mom followed in behind him.

"Clint," Grandma scolded. "You ought to be whipped for scaring everybody like that."

"Aw, come on, Grandma. This here's Hoss. He's the one I told you about that's always pulling pranks on me."

"Never mind. You damn near got him shot."

Clint threw his hands up in the air.

"But Grandma, you didn't let me explain."

It was too late for explaining. She had gone inside already. Clint looked at me like he was expecting me to punch his lights out, but I was so wore out I couldn't have beat up an egg. For some reason it felt good to just sit there on the step and rest awhile. But Clint hadn't finished razzing me yet. When he went to giggling all silly like, I couldn't help chuckling myself.

"I guess I do look kind of funny," I said as I checked out what was left of my wardrobe. "With one boot and my squashed hat and all."

"Shit! That ain't what I'm laughing at."

"Then just what the hell are you laughing at, smart ass?"

"Maybe you ought to be more careful what you pray for, Hoss."

"Huh?"

"Didn't you tell me you was praying to find a gal with a room of her own? One that was looking for a handsome guy like you?"

"Yep. I guess I did tell you that. So what?"

"Well, your prayers were answered, weren't they?"

Clint grinned so big his ears might near moved to the back of his head.

"What in the world are you talking about?"

"I'm talking about you and my Grandma. She's got a room of her own, don't she? And she thinks you're awful cute, too."

"Oh, I get it," I said after I had thought about it a minute. "Well, I guess that makes you the winner, Clint."

Port of Entry

This may be hard to believe, but in June of 69 I was in a real predicament. The rodeo season had barely started and I wasn't just broke, I was without wheels. Of course, it wasn't really my fault. You see, one night after the show, there was this big party at the Guymon Hotel in Oklahoma. For some reason, the local boys took exception to us cowboys horning in on their gals, and the only logical thing to do was duke it out. Now, from a cowboy's point of view, I guess there's nothing unusual about that. The unusual part was how I lost my truck.

I had a room at the U&I Motel about a half a mile down the road, so when the cops stormed the place I hopped in my old beater and took off. It was just like all the other trucks I had ever owned except it was a different color. It had whiskey bumps all over it and I had to pump just as hard and just as fast to get her to slow down. Stopping was another matter. Generally, I'd just let her roll until it was safe to jump out. Or if it was an emergency, I'd run her into something cheap. The something cheap part is where I got in trouble.

I was trying to put some distance between me and the do-right boys that night, and maybe I was driving a might too fast. I don't know because the speedometer was broke. And maybe I had three or four beers more than I should have. When it comes to details like that, my memory is kind of fuzzy. But I swear, until I peeled around the corner and saw that wrought iron fence around the pool, I didn't know that motel even had a swimming pool.

My vision must have been blurred, too. I didn't see a damn thing that looked cheap. My foot went plum through the floorboard and I plowed right through the fence and hit one of them multi-color sunbathing chairs. It shot straight up in the air and the patio table went up behind it. My poor ole truck was wearing the umbrella for a hood ornament. When she took out the diving board and belly-flopped into the deep end of the pool, I knew we were done for. As she started to sink, I peered out the window. All I could see was a giant tidal wave, and it was headed straight for the motel office.

The noise had woke up the manager. I seen him standing there at the office door. He didn't have on nothing but his boxers.

"What the holy hell is going on out there?"

I had to think fast. I crawled out of my truck, swam to the edge of the pool, and climbed out. I was soaked plum through and my boots were full of water. I knew I couldn't outrun him, so I screamed instead.

"Help! Help!" I yelled. "Some crazy son-of-a-bitch ran over me and drove right into the swimming pool."

The manager stepped over what was left of the fence and came toward me.

"Who the hell was it?"

I did my best to look shook up.

"I didn't catch his name. I was just sitting out here at the patio table having a smoke. The next thing I knew that crazy fool peeled around the corner, hit my table and knocked me into the pool."

"Did you get a look at him?"

"No!" I said like I was annoyed at him for asking. "I can't even swim! I was just trying to keep from drowning."

"Wait right here. I'll go call the cops. They'll want to talk to you."

As soon as he was inside and out of sight I hooked it out of there. I went back to my room and gathered up my stuff. As luck would have it, a cowboy drove up just as I was closing the door to leave.

"Hey there, buddy! Looks like you're in a hurry. Want a ride?"

I couldn't get in his truck fast enough.

"I sure do thank you, pard. My name is Dan. I sure am glad you stopped."

"Howdy." He shook my hand. "My name is Roy King. I wasn't going to stop, but I saw that wreck out by the pool as I came around the corner and then I saw you. I thought to myself, this looks pretty interesting and that ole boy looks like he could tell me the whole story."

We both chuckled.

Well, it turned out Roy was a calf roper, and his uncle was Lewis King, a stock contractor in Santa Rosa, New Mexico. When I said I knew him, Roy told me Lewis was looking for another cowboy to help haul his string to Winslow. He offered to let me spend the night with him and hitch a ride to Santa Rosa the next morning.

I never minded working for stock contractors. It didn't pay all that much, but it was a good opportunity to get to know the string, and Lewis King had a sure enough good string of bulls and horses. I got to thinking, if I was to do that for ole Lewis, I'd earn enough money to take care of the essentials and pay entry fees to the next show. It also would buy me some time to figure out how to get a new rig. Meanwhile, I could sleep in Lewis's truck.

It wasn't hard to get the job. I'd driven a truck off and on and Lewis had seen me ride in several rodeos. He knew I could handle a bucking string and I wouldn't twist off before the job was done. He hired me and said I could start the following day.

I showed up exactly when he told me to. Lewis was a stickler for being on time. I got his bucking horses loaded real handy like and he gave me the paperwork and the keys to the truck.

It was just getting dark when I got to the port of entry at the Arizona state line. Like most agriculture stations in the sixties, everybody had to stop so the inspectors could check the produce that was coming into the state. They had to make sure the fruits and vegetables weren't infested with bugs or some rare plant disease. And being as how it was so close to the Mexican border, they questioned anybody carrying livestock. I guessed that was to see if any of them was sick. Or stolen.

I had the papers for the horses in the seat right beside me. There wasn't but three or four trucks ahead of me, so it wouldn't take more than five minutes to check in and be on my way. The papers verified that all the stock had their shots, and there was a description of every animal, including what their brands were. So, the inspector's job was pretty simple. I could whiz through there and maybe even get to Winslow early enough to make a dance. I knew a gal there that was sweet on me, and if I played my cards right, I could stay over with her and maybe even borrow her car for a few days.

Life was good. I had almost forgotten about the wreck at the motel by the time I pulled up to the inspection station. I was humming a Jim Reeves tune when the inspector started walking toward my truck.

Unless I missed my guess, this guy had just come on shift. I quit humming. By the looks of that uniform, it was his first day on the job, too. It was so stiff you could have sliced beef jerky on the crease in his pants. There wasn't a speck of dust on them spit-polished boots, neither — which is pretty amazing for that part of the country — and it was a damn good thing the sun wasn't shining. That badge of his would have set the sage brush afire.

Now, I got nothing against a man that cleans up good. In fact, I've been told a time or two that I looked pretty shiny myself. I do, however, take offense to anyone who takes their job too seriously. And the look on this guy's face was entirely too business-like to suit me. I'd been through a lot of port of entries before, including this one. Usually the guy on duty made sure my papers were in order and waved me on. I had even rodeoed with a couple of them ole boys. This little feller was different, though. It was obvious he took his job real serious. He stood tall — well, as tall as a man five-four can stand — and with that hair all slicked back like Barney Fife, he would have made ole Sheriff Andy proud. Yessir!

I reached for my papers as he marched up to the truck. I got out and handed them to him. He looked up at me — way up — and then he stuck his chest out just in case I hadn't noticed his badge.

"Let's just take a look here," he said as he drew his flashlight from its holster. He started walking towards the back of the truck, shining it through the slats of the trailer as he went.

"I can't see in there. Unload those horses so I can properly identify them."

"What?"

I couldn't believe what I was hearing.

"Mister, if you want to cross my state line, you had better start unloading those horses."

I realize that some folks don't know much about horses, but this was a real dumb request. Them bucking horses all weighed thirteen to fourteen hundred pounds each. Even in the dark, you didn't have to be no equestrian genius to see they weren't somebody's saddle ponies.

"Come on, mister. There's already three other vehicles waiting behind you."

That little pipsqueak was starting to annoy me. However, I wanted to get the hell out of there, so I tried real hard to make him understand.

"These here are bucking horses, you know. Big equines with a bad disposition. They aren't barn-soured old nags. They get first-class traveling accommodations and the finest feed in the world. In return for all that, they do their dam'dest to kill cowboys. If I try to jump these animals out here in this parking lot, they're gonna think it's time to go to work."

"Mister, I don't have time for your excuses. I'm the authority here, and I said unload those horses."

I was not in the mood for a big wreck, so I tried to explain one more time.

"I'm telling you, those horses will scatter fast and furious and they'll run plum over anyone who gets in their way."

He threatened me with a cold stare.

"Look," I said real calm like, "These are Lewis King's horses. You know. The stock contractor who . . ."

"I don't care if they're Ben Cartwright's horses."

"Don't you get it? These are wild horses."

"What are you trying to pull, cowboy? Don't you think I know anything? The only reason a rodeo horse bucks is because you fasten that strap around its flank. If it weren't for that, they'd be as gentle as any other horses." He shuffled the papers, waiting for me to say something. "I read that in an article just the other day."

"Who wrote it? Ben Cartwright?"

"You're headed for big trouble," he mumbled as he started back towards the station. "If you don't do what I say, your horses aren't going anywhere."

"Buddy, you are making a big mistake."

"You've got one minute to start unloading horses. And don't call me Buddy. You're not coming through here until I've checked every one of those animals and I'm completely satisfied they're not stolen."

That did it! I had been accused of a lot of things, and I admit I was guilty of a few, but this was the first time anybody ever accused me of being a horse thief. And besides that, what's so bad about calling a feller Buddy? That there was a right friendly gesture, considering the other names I had thought of calling him. I don't know if that little feller had ever been to a rodeo or not, but he was a-fixing to be in one.

I went to the cab of the truck, pulled out a thirty-foot rope, tied a snap to the end of it, and walked back to the trailer. Barney was right behind me.

"If you insist on me jumping these animals out, you'll have to help." I handed him the coiled end of the rope. "Here. Hold this."

Barney stood at parade rest while I snapped the rope to Gun Smoke.

Gun Smoke was a saddle bronc. We had put him at the very back of the trailer for a reason. He weighed just over fourteen hundred pounds and he always had to be the first horse out. The last time someone put him at the front, as soon as the tailgate opened he ran clean over the other horses to get out of there. So, in order to protect the rest of the animals, we had loaded him last.

"This horse leaves a little fast," I said, "So you'll want to make sure you got a good grip on the rope."

Let me tell you, that ole boy took me serious. He wrapped that rope around his waist and gripped it so hard his knuckles were turning white.

I held back a chuckle and asked him, "Are you sure that's the way you want to do it, Barn . . . er, Buddy?"

He gave me that stare again.

"I've been trained to restrain dangerous criminals. I think I can hold on to one horse."

I unlatched the gate.

That horse came screaming out of the trailer like he was at the Preakness. He yanked the rope through Barney's hands so quick he didn't even have time to think about letting go. He had rope burn so bad I could smell it, and Gun Smoke didn't let up until he had hit the end of the loop. Barney let out a grunt as all the air left him. That rope had drawed up around his waist so tight he looked like a Coke bottle.

When Gun Smoke took off again, he jerked one of them shiny boots clean off Barney's foot and launched him about ten foot up in the air. That idiot came down face first on the parking lot. There was gravel spraying every which way and the dust rose up in a big cloud. After it settled some, I saw him bouncing along behind Gun Smoke like a sack of feed.

I tried to catch up.

"Don't let go," I yelled, "Or he'll get away."

I got to laughing so hard I had to sit down. That's when I lost sight of them.

I could hear ole Barney hollering, but I couldn't see a thing. Gun Smoke had drug him clear across the parking lot and into the darkness. I figured I'd give him a minute or two to think about why he was there, but when everything went silent, I decided I had better go gather Lewis's horse up and assess the damages. I wasn't all that concerned about Barney, but there'd be hell to pay if that horse was loose on the highway and got run over. Lewis sure enough would be mad. Then I'd lose my job and I'd have to start all over again.

I found the two of them near the fence that ran alongside the highway. That little feller was rolled up in a ball moaning, and Gun Smoke was standing there staring at him. He was still spooked, and he was sure curious about what he'd been dragging behind him. He lowered his head and snorted at Barney. I could tell he was looking to make his escape, so I eased up real quiet like and cut the rope with my pocket knife.

"Easy boy, easy now," I said as I led him away from Barney.

It was a good thing Gun Smoke was wore out. Those horses are only about half broke to lead. They'll follow the pick-up man back to the pen after a ride, but other than that, you're taking your life into your own hands. If he had wanted to take off, I damn sure couldn't have stopped him. Bucking horses are only used to working eight seconds at a time and, lucky for me, Gun Smoke already had exceeded his limit. He followed me to the trailer and jumped right back in.

When I got back to Barney he was halfway sitting up and leaning against the fence.

"Damn, pard," I said as I reached down to pull him up. "You sure made a hand. You might near scared that animal to death. How'd you ever hang on to him all that time? Barney was a-wobbling and a-weaving and his ole eyes rolled around like two marbles. He for sure didn't know who I was.

"I had to hang on. I was all tangled up in that rope. I couldn't have let go, even if I had wanted to."

Barney's bell had been rung but good. I kept my eye on him so he wouldn't wander off into the traffic and helped him to the station. When I got him under the lights again, one of the other inspectors saw us and came running out to see what was going on.

"Now, I know you're a man with a job to do," I said to Barney when the other feller got close enough to hear. "If you want me to get Gun Smoke back out so you can check him closer, I'll . . ."

Barney sputtered a bit and that's when his lights went out.

"What's the matter, Jenks?" asked the other inspector when Barney fell against me. "Jeez, man! Did you get run over by one them eighteen wheelers or what?"

Barney just stared into space. His mouth was hanging open but nothing was coming out of it.

"Aw, he'll be all right in a minute or two," I said. "Just knocked a little bark off is all."

The two of us carried him into the office and deposited him in a chair. What a mess! He looked like that crazy coyote in the cartoons — right after the Road Runner drops a ton of Acme Dynamite on him. I think he was in a coma. His uniform was sure enough in sad shape. The cuffs were tore plum off his shirt sleeves, and there wasn't any sign of that shiny badge. His cap was missing, too, and his Brylcremed hairdo was sticking straight up in the air. He had so much dirt smeared on his face it was hard to tell which was his ear and which was his nose.

Barney's boss tried slapping his face with cold water, but all he did was whimper, so I tried to explain what happened.

"My inspectors are highly trained individuals," the boss said when I had finished. "They handle all kinds of animals. Rodeo horses included. Now, I'm not calling you a liar, son, but unless he comes around and verifies your story, I'm gonna have to detain you until the regional manager gets here in the morning."

Just what I needed! I had tried to cooperate with these boys, but I was starting to lose my cool.

"I'm telling it exactly like it happened," I said as politely as I could. "Barney over there — I mean Inspector Jenks — ordered me to jump that trailer full of bucking horses out so he could inspect them."

Barney started shaking his finger at me and muttering, but nobody could understand a word of it. He was so comical looking his boss got to chuckling and when one of the other inspectors came into the station, he wanted to hear the whole story over again. Well, since I wasn't going anywhere, I'd just as soon tell a story as long as there was somebody who wanted to listen. I started right from the beginning, and when I got to the part about him wrapping the rope around his waist, the other feller bust out laughing.

"Are you hauling Lewis King's string?" he asked.

"Yes, sir. I am."

He kept laughing. "Well, all I can say is, it's a damn good thing you're not hauling Gun Smoke."

"Hell, I am! That's the horse that drug Barney all over the place."

"Barney?" He caught on right away. "Oh, you mean Jenks."

Barney awoke from his coma. His eyes were big as saucers and his face wasn't near so pale as it was when we drug him in there. In fact, it turned so red, I thought for a minute he was going to keel over again. Instead, he jumped up from his chair and limped into the boss's office. That was the first time I noticed he was wearing elevator boots. Only one, of course. The other one was still out in the parking lot somewhere.

"That crazy man tricked me!" he screamed at his boss. "He tried to kill me! I'm calling the state patrol! I'm going to have him arrested for murder."

Murder? Well, he had a point. He did look a whole lot like someone that had just been resurrected.

The boss's office had glass windows on two sides, and even though we couldn't hear Barney after he slammed the door and locked it, we could guess what he was saying. He was just a-ranting and a-raving into that receiver.

The boss finally banged on the window.

"Jenks! Listen to me. You can't have this man arrested. He did exactly what you told him to do."

Barney ignored him.

132

The boss threw his hands in the air and turned to me and said, "Son, I'm not going to be able to stop him. You best be on your way. I'll talk to the patrol when they get here."

Well, I don't know what ole Barney told the cops, but before I could get out of the parking lot there was a half a dozen patrol cars with red lights flashing and sirens blaring. It looked like one of them UFO landings. They had my truck surrounded and I was outnumbered. I knew I couldn't outrun them afoot, so I just climbed out of the cab and put my hands up.

Two patrolmen walked over to me. The young one didn't say nothing. I figured he was a rookie. The older feller with his gut hanging over his buckle did all the talking. Judging by the stripes on his jacket, he was a sergeant. He told me to put my arms down and then they escorted me back into the station.

Barney had calmed down some — enough to file an official report — but his boss was standing real close to him just in case he went to running off at the mouth again. You would think a little feller like that would run out of air after awhile, but he still had enough left in him to call me a name or two.

"Well, son," the old cop looked at me like I was Al Capone, "We've heard what Inspector Jenks here has to say. What's your side of the story?"

"It's real simple. I'm just trying to get this string of bucking horses to Winslow. I pulled in here and stopped and that . . ."

"Those wouldn't be Lewis King's horses. Would they?"

"Yes sir. They would."

He grinned at me, shook his head, and stared down his nose at Barney.

"Did this man tell you he was hauling bucking horses?"

"Yes sir, he did, but . . ."

"Did he have his papers?"

"Yes sir, he did, but . . ."

"And you told him he had to unload his horses. Is that right?"

"Yes sir, I did, but . . ."

"There ain't no but, Jenks! You ought to know better. You can't hold this cowboy responsible."

Barney came uncorked.

"If you're not going to do anything," he screamed, "I am! I'm going to shoot him."

Just as Barney reached for the sergeant's pistol, his boss grabbed one arm and the rookie took hold of the other. They lifted him up in the air to keep him from coming at me and that's when I started laughing. His belt had broke and when those little ole legs went to pumping, his pants slid plum to the floor.

"Hang on, Joe," the sergeant said to his partner. "I think we have a straight jacket in the squad car if we need it."

The rookie spoke up for the first time.

"Yeah. And it's just his size, too."

"Cowboy!" the sergeant hollered to me, "You get on out of here."

Boy, was I relieved! I didn't wait for him to tell me twice. I started single-footing it as fast as I could. When I stopped to open the door, he hollered again.

"Next time you talk to your boss, you tell him Don Lee said hey. Lewis is my brother-in-law."

His brother-in-law? Well, I'll be damned! This was my lucky day!

I believe that was the first and only time in my life the cops ever helped me get away from the scene of the crime. I never did find that little filly in Winslow that night, but it didn't matter none. You see, Lewis got so damn tickled about the Barney story, he made me an offer I just couldn't refuse. He had an old ranch truck he wanted to sell and, wouldn't you know it, the price was the exact same amount as my paycheck.

And that wasn't the end of my good fortune. A few weeks later I got to ride Gun Smoke. I don't know if that ole feller remembered me rescuing him from Barney or not, but he gave me one helluva ride and I won the purse that night. It wasn't a whole lot, but it was sure enough bigger than Lewis's paycheck. So, I traded that ole truck of his for a new set of wheels. Well, not exactly a new. It did have glass in the windows, though. And the radio worked real good, so I was back to humming along with Jim Reeves in no time.

Yessir, life was good.

Uninvited

Some folks just hate to go to the dentist. They get nervous and jittery at the sound of a drill. Other people hate to go to the doctor because the sight of a needle makes them all queasy. Well, I'm here to tell you, I'd rather have every tooth in my head filled and get a series of rabies shots all on the same day than go to see the banker. And I know a lot of other cowboys that feel the same way. Still, a man's got to do what a man's got to do sometimes, and one September day back in 65, that's exactly what I had to do.

☆ ☆ ☆

I had been sitting in the lobby of the local bank for thirty-five minutes, tapping the floor with the toe of my boot and trying not to swaller my chew when Cecil Hoagley finally came out of his office.

He walked up, shook my hand, and patted me on the back.

136

"Hi there, buddy," he said like we had been friends for years.

They always do that, you know.

"Morning, Mr. Hoagley."

"Dan, come on in here and let's see if we can fix you up."

For a minute I actually thought he was going to help me. I followed him into the office.

Cecil sat down in his orthopedic chair — one of them fancy leather ones I had seen advertised on TV for $900. I grabbed a metal folding type that had a nice view of Main Street.

"What can I do for you today, Dan?"

"I need to borrow a couple thousand dollars."

He leaned across that big ole mahogany desk of his and glared at me.

"Are you still with that rodeo business?"

"Not at the moment. Why?"

"Well, you know, that's just not a very stable . . ."

He paused to light up a cigar.

"Very stable what?"

Hoagley leaned back and propped his feet up on the desk. He had on a pair of them custom-made boots you see in the western wear catalogs for $300 a pair. The toes and heels were trimmed with snakeskin.

"Well," he puffed thoughtfully on his cigar, "I was going to say occupation. But it is not really an occupation. Is it now?"

"I got my RCA card, if that's what you mean. I'm a professional saddle bronc and bull rider. Just like you're a professional banker."

"Well, that's kind of like comparing apples and oranges, now. Isn't it?"

I had been in that office two minutes and already he was doing his best to insult me. Trouble was, I really needed

137

the money and I knew I sure as heck wasn't gonna get it by whipping his butt. Even if he did deserve it.

"What do you say we skip the chitchat and get right down to talking business. Can I have the money?"

"What do you want the money for? Entry fees?"

"No sir. I'm not rodeoing this winter. I want to buy some more cattle for my little spread out there on the south side of town."

"What do you have for collateral?"

"I got my place." I had to stop and think for a minute. "And my tractor, of course. And the rest of my cattle."

"Now, Dan, you know those are already mortgaged."

"And you know I ain't never missed a payment. I'll admit I throw money up and run out from underneath it sometimes. Sometimes I even give it away. And some folks say I party too much. But I ain't never risked my place."

Cecil stomped out his cigar in a big ole marble ashtray, swiveled around in that expensive chair of his, and went to staring out the window. I knew I was in for a rundown of all the reasons banks don't like to give loans to cowboys. I had heard them speeches before.

"You boys are all alike," he said, sticking his chest out like some four-star general. "Irresponsible, immature, lazy . . ."

I had heard all that before and . . . well, I just wasn't in the mood for it.

"Skip the speech, Cecil!" I stood up like I was getting ready to leave. "Are you gonna give me the money or not?"

"No need to get riled up about it, Dan. I . . ."

The phone rang. He couldn't pick up that receiver fast enough.

It was his wife. He started jawing away like I wasn't even in the room, so I sat down again and stared at all the fancy furniture in that office. I wondered how many head of cattle I could buy if I had his money. Heck!

138

If I owned that Remington original hanging on the wall, I could get a loan big enough to keep me going all winter. And next summer, too. That painting had to be worth ten grand or more.

"Dolores . . . No, Dolores! It's too late. We're not going to reschedule the reception at the Clovis Country Club. So what? It will be after nine by the time the wedding is over. Well, we'll just have to open the doors and windows. I can't find anyone to fix the air-conditioning on such short notice. What? You paid two hundred dollars for a cake? No. It will not melt, Dolores. Don't be ridiculous. Of course I love my daughter. Didn't I buy her that twenty-two hundred-dollar dress? Okay, two thousand. Yes, I know it was on sale, but have you forgotten the fifteen hundred I shelled out for the caterers?"

Damn that cheapskate! He was blowing a fortune in one night and he had the nerve to complain about cowboys being irresponsible? I could hardly believe what I was hearing.

"I know that, Dolores, but it's impossible to reschedule everything. The wedding is tonight, not next week. Besides, I put a two-hundred-dollar deposit on that hall. That's enough, Dolores. I'll be home in an hour. I have to go now. I said no, Dolores. Good-bye!"

He put the phone down and smiled proud.

"Edwina is getting hitched tonight."

I knew his daughter. Cinderella's fairy godmother couldn't have gotten that girl married a day sooner if she mortgaged Cecil's bank. She was the most stuck-up snob in school, and she was ugly to boot. I didn't even smile.

"I'm sorry." He cleared his throat. "Now, where were we? You want two thousand dollars to buy some cattle. Is that right?"

I nodded.

"Dan, I'm sorry. I just can't do it. You don't really have any collateral. Two thousand dollars is a lot of money. Now, if it was an emergency . . . if you were in the hospital or something."

"So that's it? You'd loan me the money if I was laid up but you won't loan me any to buy cattle?"

"I'm sorry. It's just too risky."

"Well, how about for something else then?"

"What do you have in mind?"

"How about loaning me a couple of grand for a wedding dress?"

"That's not funny."

"I could dress up one of my old cows. Maybe she'd corral a rich bull and produce a herd of offspring. Then I'd sell a couple of head and pay you off with interest." I stood up and put my hat on. "The odds of that happening are better than my chances of getting any money out of you."

"There's no need to go getting smart about it, Dan. I'm just doing my job."

"Yeah? Well, so are them ole boys shoveling cow shit out at the fertilizing plant, but they don't enjoy their job half as much as you do."

I stomped out of there, hopped in my pickup and headed for the station to gas her up. As I pulled up to the pump I saw Jake and Dwight, the owner, sitting out front under the awning. Jake was drinking a Coors and eating a package of Twinkies.

"Hey Hoss," Dwight said. "What can I do you for?"

When he went to get up out of his chair he caught his coveralls on a rough corner and ripped a big ole tear in the left leg.

"Dadgummit! I wished the old lady was still around to patch these things."

I wished she was, too. Dwight wasn't exactly the best-dressed businessman in town, and he damn sure wasn't no seamstress. Them coveralls must have had a dozen patches and every one was a different color.

Dwight shuffled over to the pump in his house shoes — I don't think he owned any real shoes — and I sat down in his chair next to Jake.

"Hi Hoss. Want a cold one?"

"Sure do."

He handed me a bottle and held up one of his Twinkies.

"I guess you want one of these, too."

"Hell no. How can you eat them things with beer?"

"Man, I love Twinkies. We never got any store-bought cakes when we was kids. And we couldn't hardly stomach mom's baking."

"I can believe that. Your momma thought sponge cake was made out of rubber sponges. Soap and all."

"Smart ass! Suit yourself." He shoved the cake in his mouth and tossed the wrapper on the ground. "How'd it go with ole Cecil this morning?"

"Guess."

"What'd I tell you, Hoss? You know, I think the world would be a better place without bankers and lawyers. They all think they're better than the rest of us. By the way, whatever happened to that stuck-up daughter of his?"

"I guess she finally bribed some dumb ole boy to marry her. The wedding's tonight."

"No kidding?"

"Yeah. It's gonna be a real party by the sounds of it. I overheard Cecil discussing it with his ole lady over the phone. He sure enough is spending a bundle. The wedding dress cost as much as that loan I was asking him for."

"Damn!" Jake choked. "Why didn't you marry her, Hoss? You could've pawned that dress after the honeymoon and you and me could . . ."

"I'd rather eat your momma's sponge cake."

"You are a cold-blooded son-of-a-gun!"

After he had filled my pickup and checked the oil, Dwight came over to join us. He unfolded another chair and sat down next to me.

"Say Hoss, I saw you ride last month in Lubbock. You sure looked good. Wished the ole lady had been there to see you. She sure did like to watch you ride. Did you win any money on that saddle bronc?"

"I did, but not near enough to get me through the winter."

"Dang, my watch is broke," Dwight said. "What time is it?"

"It's might near noon," Jake told him.

"Shoot!" Dwight got out of his chair almost as fast as he'd sat down. Real slow and easy like. "I gotta let ole Buford out," he groaned. "You know, the old lady never did like Buford."

Dwight was always talking about his runaway wife and we always tried to change the subject, because whenever anybody would mention Velma Pearl, he'd recount the whole incident about how she ran off to Detroit with the vacuum salesman. It wasn't that the tale itself was so bad, it was Dwight's telling it. He'd start from the day they met, which was about thirty-four years, two months and seven days ago, and then he'd go to describing every house they ever lived in, every car they ever bought, every TV show they ever watched and every petunia she ever planted. The more he talked, the more beer he drank, and the more he drank, the more he cried. Before you knew it, you'd have to haul him home and heave him into bed. So, that's why I had inquired about Buford and not Velma Pearl.

"I was just wondering where ole Buford is," I said. "How come you got him locked up, Dwight?"

Buford was half hound dog and half Saint Bernard — about the biggest canine I ever saw — and he slobbered a lot. He was friendly, too. He'd run up to perfect

142

strangers and start licking them. Then he'd shake his big ole head until they were covered with slime from head to toe. It was sort of like being dunked in a pot of boiled okra.

"I gotta keep him close to home these days," said Dwight. "Ever since Harold got him that new watchdog."

Harold owned the local wrecking yard about a half a mile down the road from the station.

"Are you trying to tell me Buford's afraid of an ole junkyard dog?" Jake asked.

"No. He sure ain't," Dwight grinned. "He's in love. That bitch is in heat and every time Buford sees her he starts to howling. It's the most woeful sound you ever heard. Harold says his neighbors have been complaining about it. And God forbid if them two have pups."

Jake was chuckling. "Why's that, Dwight?"

"Well, you know Buford ain't all that purty. But Harold's mutt is about as ugly as a critter can be. He says she's half bulldog and half Shih Tzu. I ain't never heard of that until he told it to me."

"That's one of them there bullshit dogs," Jake laughed.

"Huh?" Dwight looked confused.

"Never mind. What's her name?"

"Penelope Marie."

"Penelope Marie?" Jake and me said as we both bust out laughing.

"Yep. I think he named her after his mother. She's about half of Buford's size with curly hair on her head. It's curly on her tail and paws, too, but the rest is all kinky, sorta like . . . well, you know what I mean."

The more Jake and I laughed, the more Dwight kept talking. We weren't about to stop him either. For once in his life he had got his mind off Velma Pearl.

"She's brown in some places and black in others," he continued. "One ear sticks straight up and the other hangs flat down. Just the other day when I went over to get a part from Harold, ole Buford leaped out of the truck and started chasing her. Well, I think that dog is part thoroughbred, too. She ran like a shot. Buford had a helluva time keeping up but he didn't weaken. Of course, Harold went to worrying, so we hopped in his car to chase them. You know how silly he is about his dogs. We passed Buford at Main and First and finally caught up with Penelope Marie a mile and a half down the highway. I tell you, that's the leapingest dog I ever saw. I bet she weighs forty pounds or more, and when she gets excited she jumps just like a kangaroo. Heck, I seen her clear ole Harold's fence in a single bound."

When Dwight went to repeating himself, I interrupted him.

"Say, you ain't got a wheel to fit Pa's Ford Fairlane out back in that big ole garage of yours do you?"

"Gee, I don't know, Hoss. Let's go see. You know it's dark as night in there. Even in the daytime. Some of the neighborhood kids busted out all my windows so I boarded them up. First I gotta open the door and let Buford out to do his thing. While he's doing that, I'll grab a flashlight."

When Dwight opened the station door, Buford bolted out of there and began watering a half a dozen old tires that were leaned up against the building. Jake offered to sit and watch the pump and wait on customers while me and Dwight went out back, and as soon as Buford had irrigated the place to his satisfaction, he followed us.

That garage was big as a barn. Come to think of it, it had been a barn before the station was built. Unlike most mechanics, Dwight didn't have a lot of tools and spare parts. There was a stack of old newspapers in the west corner and a heap of empty oil cans in the north corner and that was about it. I wondered why he had a

144

rickety wood ladder leading up to the loft, because he didn't have anything up there neither. The place was so empty, our voices echoed when we talked.

"Be careful where you step, Hoss. I spilt some nails in here the other day and I'm not sure I found them all."

He turned on the flashlight just as I was coming in the door behind him and Buford almost ran over me.

"Don't let Buford in here!"

"Why?"

"Because . . ."

It was too late. That big hound shoved me clean out of the doorway and disappeared into the dark.

Dwight turned the flashlight off.

"Don't move, Hoss. I gotta find that dog and get him out of here."

"Wouldn't it be easier with the light on?"

"Nope. Here Buford," he called out. "Buford . . . oh, Buford."

No way was that dog coming out of that garage. And, big as he was, Dwight wasn't having any luck finding him in the dark.

"Damn, Dwight. Turn the light on."

"Okay," he agreed at last. "But when I find him, you gotta promise to help me get him out of here."

I promised.

When the light came on, Buford was standing there in the flashlight beam, panting and barking like he'd seen a rabbit or something.

"Watch this here," Dwight said as he waved the light back and forth across the floor.

Buford barked again and started chasing the beam. The faster the light moved, the faster he ran. That dog was jumping like a rabbit and barking and a-slobbering like he was plum loco.

"Let me do that, Dwight."

I grabbed the flashlight from his hand and aimed it at the ladder. Sure enough Buford went crazy. He slobbered so much chasing around the foot of that ladder, he slid on his butt about every other turn. I got to laughing so hard my stomach hurt.

"Man, it don't take much to entertain you, does it Hoss?" About that time Dwight slipped in the slime and split his coveralls clean up to the crotch. "Shoot! Give me that light before he tries to climb the ladder. I ain't got any wheels in here. I think you just wanted to get me out here so you could kill me."

"Don't be ridiculous, Dwight. You didn't tell me Buford liked to chase lights."

As soon as Dwight flicked the torch off, his dog headed for daylight, and this time he nearly knocked Dwight off his feet as he darted through the doorway.

Dwight was not amused.

"Hey Jake," I hollered when we got back to the station. "You ever seen Buford chase lights?"

"What are you talking about?"

"Dwight, can I take the flashlight back into the garage and show ole Jake what Buford does?"

"No! That floor is so slimy, all three of you would probably fall down, hit your heads and croak. And I sure would miss Buford if that happened. You just leave my dog alone. He's got enough to deal with thinking about his lady love down there at Harold's."

"Speaking of Harold, I got to get on over there and find that wheel for my Pa's car. You coming with me, Jake?"

"Sure. Just a minute." He dropped a slug into the vending machine and collected another package of Twinkies, stuffed it into his shirt pocket, and said to Dwight: "One for the road. Old Dan here is always trying to get me to work without feeding me."

"You call that food?" I asked.

"You just mind your own business. Let's go."

Penelope Marie started yapping as soon as we pulled up to the gate, and Harold came strutting out like the President had just arrived for a visit. Harold was a bachelor. I don't know if he ever had a date in his life, but if he treated the gals as good as he treated his dogs, he would have to beat the women off with a stick. He loved dogs. He fussed over them like some old lady, bought them fancy collars and toys, and fed them special dog snacks to make their breath smell fresh. Yessir, anyone looking for a mean and scroungy dog at this junkyard was in for a shock.

"Hey boys! What do you think of my new dog?"

To tell you the truth, that little yapper couldn't have scared a rabbit off, but she could damn sure annoy it to death with that shrill bark of hers. Personally, I could not see what Dwight's hound was so excited about. But one look at Buford and you knew he wouldn't win any dog shows either.

Being my usual polite self, I said: "She sure looks like a dandy, Harold."

Harold grinned and Jake poked me in the ribs and snickered under his breath.

Harold put his hand down to hold Penelope back while we went through the gate, but he wasn't fast enough. Or maybe Penelope was too fast. I'm not sure which. Anyway, she slipped past him and started running down the road.

"Damn that dog! She ought to be in the races. Penelope!"

Harold hollered a couple of more times before he spied Jake's Twinkies.

"Hey!" Jake protested when Harold snatched the package out of his pocket. "What are you doing with my cupcakes?"

"Watch. She'll do anything for sweets."

Harold tore open the Twinkies and that dog stopped dead in her tracks. It was like she could smell them. She turned back and stared at Harold.

"Come on, Penelope Marie." He squatted down and tried to coax her back. "I got a treat for you."

The dog cocked her head to one side and then the other, and all of a sudden she took off running like a horse headed for the feedbag. Harold held the cake just out of reach until she was inside the fence and then he closed the gate. He tossed one of the Twinkies to her and one to Jake.

Jake poked the cake in his mouth.

"Gee, thanks, Harold. Don't forget you still owe me one."

"What are you boys after today?"

"I need a new wheel for that ole Fairlane of my Pa's."

"You're about three days late. Some ole boy took the last one I had. Sorry, Hoss."

He didn't even have to look. Harold kept an inventory of every piece of junk in the place. The tires were stacked up according to size, and he parked all the old cars according to make and model. If you had to find a part, Harold's Salvage was definitely the place to go. But this just was not my lucky day.

"Aw that's all right, Harold," I said. "That means I don't have to make a trip out to Pa's. And besides that, now I got me an excuse to stay in town for the dance tonight."

Jake's eyes lit up.

"Damn, Hoss! We should have thought of that sooner. Pret' near all the women in this town are spoken for, and if you think I'm gonna dance with ole widder Pickens all night, you got another think coming."

"Well boys, whatever you do, don't you be doing anything I wouldn't do."

"Don't worry," Jake told him. "If we mess up and do something real bad I promise we'll go to confession."

Most people around those parts was Baptist and Jake was always teasing Harold about being Catholic.

"Even if you paid admission," Harold chuckled, "I doubt the priest would allow either one of you in the church."

"That's exactly why you didn't see us at Mass last Sunday," I said. "We can't afford it."

Harold just grinned and waved. This time he slipped his finger through Penelope's fake diamond collar so she couldn't follow us through the gate.

The first traffic light we hit in town was red. That was my chance to look and see if there was any stray fillies that might want to go to the dance with me and Jake. My luck was still running cold, though, and when I glanced down First Street for the second time, I'll be darned if Edwina Hoagley didn't walk out of the beauty parlor. Her hair was all piled on top of her head in a bunch of curlicues, and her face was painted up like a movie star. She was fixing to cross the street right in front of us, and I had to admit, she almost looked pretty. Well, as pretty as Edwina could look.

"Damn! If she wasn't getting married tonight, I'd ask her to go to the dance."

"Since when did a little thing like that ever stop you?" Jake grinned. "She wouldn't go with you anyway. Even if she wasn't getting hitched."

"What makes you think an ugly ole gal like that would turn me down?"

"Same reason that gal that trains the sheriff's bloodhounds won't go out with you. They're both too sophisticated for you."

Edwina started strutting across the street. She nearly jumped out of her high heels when I honked the horn, but she ignored me just the same. So, I leaned out the window and hollered at her.

"Hey Edwina! You want to see my new tattoo?"

When she saw who it was, she wrinkled her face up and said: "I don't know what makes you think I'd want to have anything to do with you, Dan Burnett. As far as I'm concerned, you are nothing but cowboy trash."

Me and Jake watched her get into her new baby blue Mustang and drive off.

"Did you hear that?" I asked.

"Hell! The whole town heard it. What are you acting so shocked for?"

"That does it! First her old man insults me and then she goes and tells the whole damn town that I'm trash."

"What do you care? She ain't your type anyway."

"What has that got to do with it? It's the principle of the matter."

"Principle?" Jake looked puzzled. "So, that's what you're calling your ego these days."

"Look, smart guy, you . . ."

"I know. I know. But let's face it, Hoss. Poor boys like you and me just got to get used to being snubbed by rich girls like her."

"But it ain't right, Jake. It just ain't right!"

Jake laughed it off, but I was still burning. That's when I got to thinking it was my turn to do some insulting.

"You still want to go dancing tonight?"

"You bet."

"Well, we're going somewheres new."

I turned left at the next light and pulled up in front of the grocery store.

"You are senile, Hoss. I thought you was going to the auto parts store."

"Forget that wheel, Jake. We got to get ready for the dance."

"I don't like that gleam in your eye. What in the hell are you up to?"

"Stick with me, pard. You'll find out."

Jake followed me into the grocery store as I explained the details of my plan.

"Better buy about six packages of them Twinkies 'cause you know you're going to eat half of them before we get there. And don't forget the beer."

I took Jake back to his place after awhile and told him to meet me in front of the Methodist Church at eight o'clock. Then I drove out to Dwight's garage.

Buford started whining at the door when I lifted up the dead battery that was leaning against the east wall. That's where Dwight hid the key to his office.

"Hey old boy," I whispered. "How would you like to take a ride?"

Buford panted excitedly and slobbered all over my boots.

"Thanks a lot, buddy."

I grabbed Dwight's flashlight off his desk, locked the door behind us, and set the key back under the battery. Buford followed me to the truck and jumped right in the back like Dwight had trained him to do. But I was afraid he might jump out and get lost, so as much as I hated to do it, I opened the passenger door and coaxed him up front with me.

I parked my truck behind Jake's place, which was only a half a block from the church, and walked over to his pickup. He was in the passenger seat and Penelope Marie was sitting on his lap.

"Hey pard, did she give you any trouble?"

"No. I just walked up to the gate and opened a package of them Twinkies. Didn't even have to unhook the latch. Soon as I put the key in the lock, she cleared the fence. Then I tossed one of them little cakes in the front seat and she jumped in after it."

"If she does that every time, we got it made. But we had better keep a couple of packages handy, just in case she forgets her lines later."

"Good idea. So, how did you get into Dwight's station to get Buford?"

"With the key."

"You know where the key is?"

"Sure enough."

"He never told me where he hides it."

"You must be the only person in town that don't know. I bet he don't tell you 'cause he's afraid you'll rob the vending machine."

"Right. And he ain't afraid of you walking off with his prize hound?"

"We don't have time to discuss it now. Look! Here they come."

The wedding party had arrived. Edwina was wearing a snow-white dress that dragged along behind her for about a half a block, and a herd of kids with baskets full of rose petals was following behind that. I swear every cheerleader from her graduating class was a bridesmaid, and it looked like the whole football team had volunteered to be the groomsmen and ushers. There was more flowers than at a funeral and every fancy car in town was parked along the street in front of the church.

Jake and me watched the crowd climb the steps and disappear behind the heavy wooden doors. We could hear the organ playing, and when the sun went down, the lights started shining through the stained glass windows. It was sure enough a peaceful evening. For awhile.

It was dark when the doors flew open and Edwina and her new husband burst out onto the porch. The crowd threw enough rice to feed all of China and Edwina damn near knocked out one of the bridesmaids when she tossed that big bouquet of hers. When the newlyweds got into a limousine and drove to the country club, everyone else followed. Including me and Jake.

We parked out behind the hall and waited. It was just like Cecil had said on the phone that morning. The caretaker had opened all the windows and doors, trying to get a crosswind in there to cool the place off. The guests were mighty thirsty and they were drinking champagne like it was water. After awhile the band started playing and in no time at all everybody was dancing and laughing, and generally acting happy and unconcerned.

When Cecil started waltzing with the other men's wives, I knew it was time. I gave Jake the signal, he pulled up close to the back door that led into the kitchen, and I drove up and parked directly behind him. That's when Buford spotted Penelope Marie. He was grunting so loud I thought for sure the caterers would hear him. But, lucky for us, they had drunk so much champagne they didn't hear a thing. Hell, they barely could walk.

"Jake," I whispered through the crack in the window. "I don't know how long we're gonna be able to keep these two apart. We sure as heck can't leave them locked up in the trucks. It's too damn hot. Are you sure you know where the fuse box is?"

"Oh yeah. I helped my uncle rewire this place last year. It won't take but a minute."

I got out of my truck and grabbed a package of Jake's Twinkies. Penelope knew what I had in my hand and she was scratching the window just a-begging me for that piece of cake. Meanwhile, Jake snuck up to the metal box outside the kitchen door, and a few seconds later every light in the place went out. I heard a couple of gasps and then complete silence. I tossed two Twinkies onto the kitchen floor, and as soon as Jake opened the door of his truck, Penelope leaped out and made a bee-line for the club.

Everything had been pretty quiet up until then, but I had a feeling things was about to change.

"Eeek! What is that?" cried Mrs. Hoagley. "Cecil, some kind of beast just ran over my foot."

"Where is it?"

"Oooh no. I can hear it, can't you?"

"What happened to the lights? Does anyone know where the lights are?"

I recognized Cecil's voice.

"No one move!" he yelled.

That's when I opened the door of my truck. Buford jumped out and landed with a thud. The ground shook all around me like we was having an earthquake. Then, with one mournful howl, he put his big ole nose down and headed straight for the door. He'd picked up Penelope's scent and he was hot on her trail.

"Oh my God what is that?" a woman screeched.

I grabbed the flashlight out of the seat, wiped the slime off on my pants, and headed for an open window. Jake was right behind me and boosted me up so I could reach the sill. I was just about ready to shine that light on the party when someone inside lit a match. It was just a tiny flame but it was enough to get Buford excited. I stretched to get a better look, and then Jake let go of me and I hit the ground like a rock.

"Shit!" Jake was wiping his hands on his jeans. "You sure are one slippery customer. What you got all over them blue jeans. Monkey grease?"

I didn't have time to explain the slobber.

"Shut up and listen, Jake."

We didn't have to see anything to know what was going on in there. Every time we heard a thud, we knew that Buford had ran clean over somebody and knocked them down. And we didn't have any trouble figuring out who was talking either.

"Oh my god! Daddy, turn on the lights. Daddy! Hurry," Edwina whined. "My wedding is ruined. Absolutely ruined!"

"Where's the caretaker? Will one of you drunks please find the damn fuse box."

"Cecil," his wife pleaded, "Please don't curse. Can't you find the fuse box yourself?"

"How would I know where it is, Dolores?" The guests were starting to make a lot of noise and Cecil was getting edgy. "Everybody shut up!"

It took three or four minutes for things to calm down. Jake and me figured that was on account of Buford. Penelope was having too much fun to pay him any mind.

I looked at Jake. "Do you think them two have had enough time to get acquainted?"

"Yeah. She's probably gobbled up that Twinkie by now. I'll go throw the lights back on."

Jake and me found a window that was a little closer to the ground so when the lights came on we got a real good view of the damage. What a mess! Tables were turned up, flower vases were tipped over, and the guests were either standing on chairs or hiding under tablecloths. Half of them were covered in Buford's slobber, and the entire floor was streaked with slime.

"My cake!" Edwina screamed when she saw the flattened wreck on the only table in the place that was still standing.

Penelope must have heard her say cake, because she was on top of that table in the blink of an eye, her curly tail wagging happily as she lapped up the white frosting. When Buford caught sight of his beloved, he headed straight for the table and put his big ole paws on the end of it. That darn thing collapsed and Penelope and the cake came sliding right down there in front of him. Buford didn't waste any time getting down to business. He positioned himself behind Penelope, and as she licked the last of the frosting off her lips, the two of them started getting it on like they was the happy couple, right there in front of everybody.

"Daddy," Edwina cried when she saw the plastic bride and groom hanging out of Penelope Marie's mouth. "That bitch stole my cake top."

Mrs. Hoagley was frantic. She reached into a bowl of cocktail peanuts and threw a handful at the dogs. Buford didn't even notice. As for Penelope . . . well, I don't think she was real happy with Dolores, but she wasn't exactly in a position to do anything about it either. Buford had her grounded.

The older women gasped, turned their heads and covered their eyes, and a couple of bridesmaids headed for the ladies room. Dolores continued to throw her peanuts and the children went to pointing at the dogs and giggling. Most of the men thought it was the funniest thing they had ever seen. But not Cecil. He went crazy.

"Doesn't anyone have a gun?"

"Now, dear. Calm down or you'll have a heart attack."

The groom was the one that finally saved the day.

"I called the sheriff," he said as he wiped the muck off his tuxedo. "He's on his way."

"Who's responsible for this?" Cecil wanted to know. "I'll kill the son-of-a-bitch!"

"Please, dear. For heavensake, take one of your pills . . . or something."

Jake and me were rolling on the ground laughing when we heard the siren.

"Hell, Hoss, we gotta get out of here."

"What about Buford and Penelope?"

"No need to worry about them two. I think they're gonna live happily ever after."

"That's not what I mean. The sheriff knows whose dogs they are. He checks Dwight's station and the salvage yard might near every night on his patrol."

Jake tugged at my shirtsleeve.

"Come on, Hoss. We got to go. Now!"

We had just cruised past the front of the hall when the sheriff pulled up. I really wanted to stick around to see what was going to happen next, but Jake was right. If we was to get caught, there'd be hell to pay. Besides, ole Hoagley probably wouldn't even let me in the bank again, let alone talk to me about a loan.

If you know how small towns are, I guess you probably figured out by now that it didn't take long for us to hear the end of the story. Yessir, we heard the whole thing down at the cafe the next morning. Our waitress was a bridesmaid — one of them that didn't run off to the ladies room. According to her, the sheriff and his deputies threw a couple of tablecloths over Buford and Penelope, and told all the old ladies and children to go outside. When they got the dogs separated, they took them home to their owners and questioned Dwight and Harold about the incident. But they knew right off that it wasn't the kind of crime them ole boys would be involved with. So, they just told Cecil it must have been them neighbor kids of Dwight's — the ones that had busted the windows out of his garage. Of course, the sheriff was still investigating the case on account of Dwight couldn't tell them exactly which kids was the culprits.

If I had my guess, Dwight was probably proud of Buford. As for Harold, well he's the type that gets all embarrassed when folks go to talking about nuptials and such. Even if they had suspected me and Jake, neither one of them ever would have told the sheriff. No sir, they didn't say a word. Not that day, not ever. The sheriff and his deputies had their suspicions, too, because they was used to our little pranks. But none of them said so out loud. That's just how things work in a small town.

After the uproar had settled down some, Jake and me learned that Dwight and Harold really had figured out that we was the ones responsible. I can still see ole

Dwight leaning back in his chair and grinning like a cat that had just swallered a canary.

"You know boys, me and ole Harold here have been wanting to go fishing in Ruidoso for the last five years. Problem is, we can't never afford to leave our places unattended long enough to get away. You know how it is when you're in business for yourself."

"That's right," Harold said. "We want to stay up there a week or more. Relax a bit."

"The way I got it figured," Dwight continued, "We can either find us a couple of enterprising young men to look after things for us, or we can go see ole Cecil Hoagley and ask him to float us a loan to hire somebody. But you boys know how stingey he is. Ain't that right, Hoss?"

I looked at Jake and Jake looked back at me. We knew right then what we was gonna have to do.

Jake spoke up first.

"Hell, Dwight. No sense you hiring somebody. If you was to leave me the key to the vending machine, I'd pump gas for you for a week."

Dwight just nodded. It was a done deal.

I looked over and saw that Harold was waiting for me to say something.

"You know, Harold, I always wanted a chance to scrounge around your salvage yard. No telling what I might find. No sir. I wouldn't mind helping you out for a week. Not at all."

Harold had a real satisfied look on his face. In fact, we all looked happy with the situation because ... well, you see, that's how things are handled in a small town.

Bell of the Ball

Sometimes a rodeo cowboy's luck is so bad he is forced to lay up awhile so his body can heal. Trouble is, it ain't always easy to find somebody willing to give you a place to hole up long enough to mend what's broke, bent, mashed or jarred loose, or at least stuck back together good so you don't rattle when you walk. Like most fools that need a kind heart from time to time, I usually could find a cute little buckle bunny to feel sorry for me. And if I was lucky, she might even wrap me up and take me home with her, too. Just in case you're wondering, buckle bunnies are them gals that follow rodeos and chase cowboys. They got that name because they're always looking for the guy with the fanciest belt buckle. Yessir, the next best thing to having a good line is to wear a showy buckle. Sometimes I think them gals don't even care what a man looks like. If he's wearing a big shiny buckle, chances are he'll have to beat the women off with a stick. I guess that's how come I always got tangled up with so many of them. I had me a pretty good line, I always wore my biggest buckle, and I never carried a stick. I'll bet I surrendered a dozen buckles during my rodeo days. I never minded them girls hanging around, even if it *meant I had to hold up my britches with a string. I got to admit, though, some of them ole buckle bunnies was plug ugly. I even seen a few that could scare a cowboy to death on a dark night. But most of them had a heart the size of the Ponderosa, and when I needed a little TLC, I sure was grateful for them big-hearted ones.*

☆　☆　☆

The San Angelo rodeo was usually a money-maker for me, but in March of 68 it caused me nothing but misery. The dang bull I was riding hit me on the side of my knee just as I was getting up. I managed to crawl back to the chutes but I darn near collapsed once I got there. Every time I put any weight on that leg, the pain brought tears to my eyes. It was for sure I wasn't going to be able to walk out of there on my own. That sucker swolled up big as a fat lady's grocery cart. Anyway, I decided to stay where I was till the show was over and I could find someone to give me a hand.

I thought I might never hear the last buzzer of the night. I was standing there on one leg like one of them orange flamingos. In fact, I had stood like that so long I got to craving fish. The first person that looked like he might help me was another bull rider by the name of Jumpy. Now, Jumpy wasn't his real name, of course. Although, it could have been because his momma told him he was conceived in the back seat of a 39 Buick that didn't have no shocks. The other cowboys had hung that handle on him because he was the punchiest man that ever rode a bull. Come to think of it, I never did ask what his real name was. Jumpy suited him and I guess that's why it stuck.

Jumpy helped me hobble to my car and held the door open while I eased in behind the wheel.

"Are you hurt bad, Hoss?"

"Well I sure ain't hurt good. Damn this makes me mad! Just when I was riding good. Hope my luck's better at the dance tonight."

"At the dance?" Jumpy looked at me like I'd just flipped my switch. "You ain't in no condition for dancing, Hoss."

"I know that. I got to find me a nice little buckle bunny is all. You know. One of them types that is crazy about cowboys and has more sympathy than sense."

"Good luck!" Jumpy laughed. "I'll bet all the best looking ones will be lined up just a-waiting to tango with a cripple like you."

"Hell, I can dance better on one leg than you can on two. How much do you want to bet?"

"I don't want to take advantage of a wounded man, Hoss. I'll tell you what I'll do."

Now, I was grateful for Jumpy's help, but I didn't know if I could trust him. Just when you figure he's thinking one way, he takes off in an entirely different direction. Like I said, his name suited him real good.

"You mean you ain't gonna take a sure bet, Jumpy?"

"Naw. You take it easy tonight. Have a few beers and tell some of those famous stories of yours. Enjoy the music and leave the dancing to me."

"You're scared I'll horn in on your women. Ain't that right?"

"Scared of a cripple?" He grinned. "Hoss, you know what a generous man I am. Why, when I get one or two of them gals worn down a little, I'll send them your way. You ought to be able to handle them after I'm done with them."

"That's what I like about you, Jumpy. Always willing to let the next guy have your leftovers."

Jumpy waved and headed for his truck.

"See you at the dance, Hoss."

The Road to Ruin Bar was just outside the San Angelo city limits. It was a roller rink in its heyday, so it had plenty of room for dancing — and all them other things that can happen when a bunch of cowboys gets juiced up. I wiggled out from behind the steering wheel, planted my good leg down on the ground, and hoisted myself up. By the sounds of things the party was already going full blast, so I single-footed it across the parking lot, headed for the first empty table I saw, and plopped myself down. I sure hated to waste a good band, but my ole knee was just a-throbbing. I was ready for a cold one.

It was hard to tell where Jumpy was sitting. He already was trying to wear out the dance floor. I don't think he had sat down since he got there. That boy wasn't a good dancer but he sure was fast. The soles of his boots were just a-smoking, and that gal he was swinging around was panting like she was about to foal.

I was sitting there rubbing my leg and feeling a might sorry for myself when an old feller at the next table leaned over and asked me if I wanted a beer.

"You ever seen a cowboy that didn't?" I replied.

"Nope! By the way, partner, my name is Hank. And you're Hoss, right?"

"Right. How'd you know that?"

"Saw you at the rodeo tonight. You made a hell of a ride on ole Caboose. Those judges damn sure didn't mark you like they should have."

"No shit! That ole bull hasn't been rode but once all year. He's a bad ox to make the tooter on."

"Yeah. He's an ornery son-of-a-bitch all right. I heard they named him Caboose because he's always the last one out of the arena. Right behind the ambulance. Speaking of ambulance, looks like you ought to have someone check out that knee of yours."

"Naw. It's swolled up is all. Ain't the first time. But I was hoping to make some money at this show and it looks like I ain't gonna win a dime. Hell, I should be leading the bull riding by now instead of being fourth place."

"That's the way it goes sometimes, Hoss. Rodeo ain't changed any. Hell, when I was going down the road twenty years ago, I was starved half to death all the time. But I rarely missed the dance. Used to could cut a rug in those days. Nothing could make me forget my rodeo troubles quicker than a cold beer, a hot band and a pretty little filly to twirl around the dance floor."

"Well, I sure enough won't be doing any dancing tonight. I was hoping to find a gal that has some nursing skills. One to put me up for a week or two. But it's damn hard to impress a gal if you can't dance. Hell, even if I could make it out to the floor, ole Jumpy's already worn a groove in it. The way my luck's been running, I'd probably trip and bust my other leg."

Jumpy was dancing with his third partner, and that little gal already looked like she was about to drop.

"I been watching him," Hank chuckled. "He's not real smooth but he's damn sure rapid. Isn't that the same bull rider that bounced around on ole Moonshine tonight?"

"Yep, that's Jumpy, all right."

Hank tilted his head and eyeballed my leg.

"You think that thing is broken?"

"If it is, it won't be the first."

"How many bones have you broken, Hoss?"

I had to think about that one a minute.

"I don't rightly know, but it'd probably be a whole lot easier to show you the ones that ain't been broke."

"You're in good company. I gave up counting myself."

Hank ordered us a couple of more cold ones.

"Thanks for the beer," I said. "You know, I guess my Pa ain't so dumb after all. He told me once, a man's got to be plum crazy to want to ride bulls for a living."

"Ain't that funny." Hank got a real nostalgic look in his eye. "My Pa told me the same thing. I never would admit it to him, but looking back, I think he was smarter than most of us. Bulls, bucking horses, you name it. There ain't a one that won't try to kill a cowboy. But once rodeo's in your blood there's no getting over it. My folks tried to get me to quit from the beginning. They begged me to give it up even after I got married. And my old lady did everything she could to get me to stop, too. She didn't understand either. None of them did. A cowboy ain't gonna give it up until he's good and ready."

"Or too broke up to do it any more."

"Sometimes that ain't even enough to stop him. Hell, there were times I didn't know if I had enough working parts left to hang on to a bull. But I always managed to do it somehow. There's nothing else I know like the feeling you get when the buzzer goes off and know you've made a good ride. I don't know what it is. I can't explain it."

"I know what you mean, Hank. I have tried my dam'dest to explain it to my Pa. But regular folks don't have a clue what we're talking about, do they?"

"Nope. And I'll tell you another thing. They don't have as much fun as cowboys, either." Hank took a swig and glanced at the dance floor. "Look at ole Jumpy out there. That boy's having the time of his life. That must be one of those new dances. You ever seen anything like that before?"

"Hell, that ain't no new dance," I laughed. "That's the way Jumpy does the two-step."

The longer I sat there chewing the fat with old Hank the more something seemed familiar about him.

"Say, you wouldn't happen to be related to Henry Wilcox, would you?"

He grinned. "One and the same."

"Damn! I heard plenty about your little exploits."

"You mean to tell me those old stories are still circulating?"

"Oh yeah."

"Well, I guess you could say I have done a couple of notable things in my life."

"Is that story about the hotel in Denver true?"

"You better believe it!"

"Man, I'd love to hear that again. You got time to tell it?"

"I got all the time in the world, Hoss, but that tale just isn't all that good. You sure you wouldn't like to find a buckle bunny willing to dance a slow one with you?"

"Nope. It ain't no use even looking. Jumpy's got all them gals wound up so tight, they'll never slow down enough for me tonight."

"Bartender!" Hank hollered. "Better bring us some more beer. This guy wants me to tell him about that time we went to the stock show in Denver."

Apparently the bartender knew Hank. He was eager to hear the story, too. He got one of the barmaids to cover for him and brought a whole sixpack to our table.

"Here you go, Hank. These are on the house. As long as you don't mind if I join you."

"Make yourself to home," Hank said as the bartender pulled up a chair. "Soon as I wet my whistle I'll get started."

Hank chugged down half a bottle of Coors and cleared his throat.

"Back when I was rodeoing," he began, "I never did hang around any one town too long. Not long enough to get to know anybody so good that I'd remember them more than a day or two. But Denver was different. I had heard them folks up there was real hospitable. They sure enough were. In the beginning, anyway. We had gone up there for a stock show one winter, and there wasn't any place to stay except for this fancy hotel downtown. It was called the Flur du Loon, or something French like that. The manager seemed real happy to see us. Even had a fellow carry our bags up to the room and everything.

After we got settled, a bunch of us went looking for something to do. Well, I guess I don't have to tell you, it didn't take long for us to get bored with city life. I think we were thrown out of every bar in town before midnight, and since it was a little too cold to be wandering the streets, we decided to go back to the hotel and hang out in the lobby. We were all about half drunk by that time — stumbling around and falling into the tables and chairs and things — when some fancy folks took exception to us being there. I guess they thought we didn't exactly fit in, although they never did come right out and say so. They started pointing and whispering like we had just escaped from a mental institution.

"Well, I thought that was kinda rude, so me and this ole calf roper decided we'd point and whisper, too. One ole blister had a lot to point and whisper about. She was twice the size of her husband and she had on one of those fur coats that made her look even bigger. I swear, she looked like she had a whole pack of coyotes clinging to her. And that cockeyed fur hat on her head reminded me of a dead possum. She was wearing white gloves and bracelets that clanged like a fire truck. There was an alligator purse hanging over one arm, and tucked under the other was one them almost dogs. You know the kind with the shaved butt and fuzzy ears."

Me and the bartender was carrying on like a pair of fools. Hank was sure enough causing a stir. He paused for another swig and four more cowboys pulled up another table and some extra chairs. They figured we was having so much fun they decided to quit dancing and join us.

"I thought I heard you talking about my ole lady," one cowboy said to Hank.

"Yeah. The gal with the shaved butt," his buddy kidded him.

We all had a good laugh and then I asked Hank what the woman's husband looked like.

"Well, he was a real fashionable sort of guy, too. He had on one of those penguin suits. Come to think of it, he was about the same size as a penguin. Up next to her, that is. Me and the calf roper agreed they were the most ridiculous looking couple we had ever seen, and after awhile our pointing and whispering turned to giggling and snorting. I guess I don't need to tell you how good cowboys are at that. Specially the snorting part. Trouble is, I had me a big ole chew, and I was getting desperate for some place to spit.

"You know, those high-priced hotels are not all that convenient sometimes. I looked all around that lobby and there wasn't a spittoon in sight. So I climbed up the spiral staircase to see if there was one on the balcony. There wasn't. But there was a big mirror hanging on the wall up there, and when I saw my reflection in that thing, it got me to laughing so hard I almost lost it right then and there. I looked like a chipmunk.

"I started back down the stairs, and that's when I spotted a big brass pot at the bottom. It was full of daffodils. I guess that's how come I hadn't seen it before. Except for the flowers, it looked just like my spittoon at home. I figured I could miss the daffodils and hit that pot and nobody would be the wiser. I hung on to the banister so I wouldn't lose my balance, and leaned over as far as I could. Then I spit.

"Well, I don't know if I was dizzy from holding my breath or what, but for some reason my aim was off. And wouldn't you know it . . . that ole fur ball was standing right next to those flowers. When she saw my tobaccy dribbling down the daffodils, she puffed up like a toad. 'Oh, Theodore!' she cried out to the penguin. 'Those cowboys are so crude! Isn't there something you can do? Surely the manager will ask them to leave when he sees that!'

"All of a sudden there was a dozen or more people gathered around the bottom of the stairs. They were all decked out like they were going to a banquet and every one of them was making unkind remarks about my hat and boots. That didn't bother me too much, but when they started discussing my upbringing and insulting my Ma and Pa, that's when I decided to give them a real cowboy salute."

Hank reached in his pocket for a big ole cigar and the bartender lit it. Meanwhile, two more cowboys and their girlfriends pushed a table up next to Hank's and loaded it down with cold beer. Jumpy was still dancing up a storm. He hadn't run out of partners yet and even the band was getting used to that crazy beat of his. Either that or they were starting to feel their beer. It didn't really matter much to me. This was the best story I'd heard in quite awhile. My mind was off my sore knee and I had lost interest in dancing. I told Hank to go on and tell us about his cowboy salute.

"Well, I'll tell you," he continued, "If that was the only kind of hospitality those Denver folks had to offer, I was going to teach them some Texas manners real quick. I wasn't going to stand there and take any more of their insults. I reached down in my boot and whipped out my gun. 'It ain't polite to call a man crude,' I said as I pointed that snub-nose 38 at the penguin."

One of the buckle bunnies was getting excited.

"Oh no!" she squealed. "What did he do?"

"Nothing." Hank puffed on his cigar and grinned.

"Nothing?" the girl repeated suspiciously.

"He was froze to the floor," laughed Hank. "All of them were. Of course, my buddies were hollering for me to shoot, but I had more sense than to do something stupid like that. Unless he was threatening to steal my truck, or my wife, or something else like that . . . well, a cowboy could get in real trouble for shooting another man. Besides, I had not had a lot of target practice with that pistol and there was a good chance I'd hit somebody down there I liked. So, I held her straight up in the air and shot out the lights in the chandelier instead."

"Then what?" everybody wanted to know.

"That's when I got my revenge. The ole fur ball let out a gasp and fainted dead away. And that stupid dog of hers scooted across the floor and ran smack dab into the daffodil pot. That thing tipped over and spilled water everywhere. Hell, it almost drowned the old girl. I reckon she thought she was bleeding to death, because she came up off that floor just a-screaming. 'Theodore!' she yelled. 'He shot me. Help!' Theodore was gone. That little weasel was nowhere in sight. He'd stormed out of there with the rest of their fancy friends and left his wife to fend for herself. The only person willing to help her was the bellhop, and when he tried to quiet her down, her dog bit his ankle and pissed on his shoe.

"It sounded like a riot was happening in that lobby. The bellhop was hollering 'Fifi, Fifi, Fifi' trying to get at the dog so he could kill it, Missus High Society was bawling like a spoilt child, and us cowboys were standing around laughing and generally enjoying the show. I guess it wasn't hard to tell who the culprits were. The hotel manager came to investigate after a minute or two and I tell you, he took a real dim view of me blowing holes in his chandelier. It had been awhile since I heard a gentleman cuss like that. Nobody was going to teach him any manners. He was raging like a crazed bull. As soon as we heard the sirens, we high-tailed it out of there and never once looked back. I don't think any of us has been back to Denver since."

"Must be the high altitude that disagrees with folks up there," I chuckled.

"I don't know what it is," Hank grinned. "But there definitely was something in the air that removed their sense of humor that night."

The bartender was all red-faced from laughing and the rest of the audience was plum tickled. A guy from Las Vegas ordered a quart of tequila and offered a shot to anyone who'd tell their favorite rodeo story. I even told one myself, but we all had to admit, none of them came close to topping Hank's.

Thanks to the tequila, I soon forgot all about my bad knee. I seen Jumpy was still going strong. He had two gals scrapping over his buckle, and one of them was kinda purty, so I decided to try one dance before the band quit.

"Hey Hank," I said as I stood up to test my leg, "Do you think I'm man enough to take one of Jumpy's women away from him?"

"Would you look at that fool," Hank slurred. "Don't he ever stop?"

About that time I saw a pair of bull bells tacked to the post next to our table. They were hooked together with an old coat hanger that was twisted around a nail.

"The only thing that'd stop that cowboy from dancing is ringing them things," I said to Hank. "Jumpy's got a thing about bull bells. Back about five years ago, a bull stomped him so bad he was in the hospital for a month and he ain't never forgot it. I swear that man can be sitting flat on his butt behind the chutes and someone even jingles the change in his pocket, ole Jumpy's up in a flash. All it takes is for someone to drag his bells out of this warbag and holler 'Watch the bull!' Jumpy will clear the fence before you can even blink."

"That right?" Hank grinned.

"That's the truth," I assured him. "But I wouldn't be getting any ideas if I was you. Jumpy ain't real tall but he's stout like an ox and tough as rawhide. I seen him whip hell out of three cowboys at one time. He can't stand for someone to tease him."

Hank raised an eyebrow and downed another jigger of tequila. It was just then that the band announced their break, and I figured it was as good a time as any to make a trip to the men's room. I passed Jumpy on the way but I don't think he even saw me. His partner was wrapped around him like a snake. I watched as they slow-danced across the floor and headed over toward Hank's table.

When I came out of the men's room, Jumpy and his little gal were leaning up against the post where the bells were hanging. Ole Hank was eyeballing them like a cat watching a pair of mice. He slinked out of his chair, tiptoed over in their direction and unhooked the bells real quiet and slow. Then, when Jumpy leaned that gal against the post and laid one on her, Hank hooked the coat hanger — bells and all — to Jumpy's belt loop. As soon as the lovebirds came up for air, Hank yelled: "Watch out for the bull!"

Well, Jumpy put on his best show of the night. That ole boy went up and sideways at the same time. He was knocking over bottles, tables and bodies trying to outrun those damn bells. When he headed for the bandstand, that's when Hank snuck behind the bar and turned out the lights.

It was hard to imagine what was going on in the dark. I had never heard such a commotion in all my life. There was people running in all directions, knocking each other over and hitting anyone that got in their way. Of course, we all knew where Jumpy was. He sounded like a mobile junk shop, clanging around looking for a way out of there. When he finally found the door, he knocked the hinges plum off and it fell out into the parking lot. The noise suddenly stopped and all eyes turned toward the doorway where Jumpy was standing.

There was dead silence and the glow ...ghts from the movie house across the street ... look real eerie and mean like.

"Who's the son-of-a-bitch hung ...e dumb-ass bells on my belt?" He had their attention and he knew it. "One of you better fess up, or I'm gonna whip all your butts."

He wasn't that tough, of course. But I knew Jumpy, and there wasn't nobody in that place big enough to stop him from trying. Least of all me. So I stumbled over near the bar and found me a place to sit down. Trouble was, that particular chair just happened to belong to some other ole boy's wife, and he took offense to my butt being parked in it. I wasn't really in the mood for an argument, but when he went to insulting me I just stood up and threw it at him.

Now, I sure didn't want to cause a wreck. Honest. And I sure didn't have anything against the bartender. But that damn knee of mine gave out, I lost my balance, and that chair went sailing across the room and hit the bartender in the back. I guess he thought Jumpy had throwed it at him, so he picked it up and smacked Jumpy upside the head with it. Everybody turned on poor ole Jumpy after that. Everybody except Hank, that is. I watched him make his escape out the back door.

While I was pondering on how to get out of there before I did any more damage to that leg of mine, a skinny little guy with an oversize Stetson blind-sided me with a sucker punch. I was so mad I knocked him clear out from under that hat. When he landed on his back, I reached down to finish him off and he bit down hard on my thumb. Damn that hurt!

All of a sudden the lights came back on. Man, that little fart had big teeth! He was chewing on my thumb like a dog chews a bone. When he went to growling, I grabbed him by the throat with my free hand and squeezed hard as I could on his windpipe. He let go of my thumb real quick, but soon as I turned him loose he kicked me in the shins with them pointy little boots of his. That sent me to my knees — the very last place I wanted to be.

I've been in the wrong place at the wrong time. I've been punched, powdered, rocked, rolled, chopped, minced and diced. But no prior combat experience prepared me for the next battle. When I clobbered that little feller with a bottle his wife came to his rescue. Shit! She landed on my shoulders like a pair of sledgehammers.

Remember that nursery rhyme about Jack Sprat? Well, this woman was Mrs. Sprat times two. She was big as all of Texas and she was dressed up like a circus tent. That blimp was wearing at least twelve yards of petticoats underneath her skirt, and she parachuted down on top of me before I could get out of her way. She grabbed the bottle I had clobbered her husband with and went to whacking me on the head with it. The knots were sprouting up like popcorn. I tell you, there's no better weapon than a beer bottle. They don't break like in the movies. No sir. You can beat a man upside the head all night before you have to reload. Even a hard-headed feller like me don't stand a chance against a beer bottle. But lucky for me, her aim wasn't too sharp and she smashed her weapon into a table leg.

By that time I was getting short of breath, and I was starting to see things under that tent that I didn't recognize. I had to make my move soon or it was for sure I was going to pass out under there. I yanked the skirt off my face and pulled myself under the table where fatso couldn't get at me. It wasn't going to be easy crawling, but I didn't have any other choice. I sucked up some fresh air and headed toward the door. That's when I saw Jumpy coming for me. He was hurdling tables and bodies like he was training for the Olympics.

"Damn you, Hoss!" he screamed. "Where the hell have you been hiding, you chicken shit."

I guess he had decided that it was my fault he got the stuffing kicked out of him. It was decision time again. One of us was going to be wearing a toe tag by morning, and unless I was due for a miracle, it was gonna be me.

"You need a hand?" a big voice came from above.

It was Jerico standing next to me. Jerico was a great big bull-dogger from Odessa — broad as a barn and just about as smart. Boy, was I glad to see him.

"Hey Jerico!" I looked up at him and smiled. "See that knot-headed bull rider over yonder?"

"Jumpy? What about him?"

"What about him?" I said like I was surprised he would ask. "He told me this afternoon that you was too damn big and ugly to hang out at the rodeos. Said that you was giving cowboys a bad image."

Jerico looked a might more confused than usual.

"Jumpy said that?"

"Yep. And that ain't all. I heard him say you was the dumbest bull-dogger he ever met and he was going to whip your butt first chance he got."

When Jumpy hopped over the last broken chair between me and him, Jerico stopped him dead in his tracks. He picked that ole boy up by the neck, held him in the air and shook him like a box of Cornflakes.

"Call me big and ugly, will ya?" he growled. "I'll tell you who's giving cowboys a bad name."

Jerico didn't give poor Jumpy a chance to deny the allegations. One shot to his face and that cowboy was out like a light.

When Jerico took his fist out of Jumpy's mouth, two teeth were welded to his knuckles.

"Shit!" I said to Jerico. "You didn't have to kill him."

"He's just resting," he grinned. "Better not be talking about me like that no more, though."

Jerico reached in his back pocket for his hand-kerchief, wrapped the teeth up in it and stuck them in Jumpy's shirt pocket.

"He ain't dead, is he?" Jumpy's girlfriend asked.

"No ma'am. I just give him what he had coming is all." Jerico grabbed a half-empty bottle of beer and held it above Jumpy's head. "I'll wake him up for you if you want me to."

"Oh no," she said real sweet like. "He's probably tired. We been dancing real hard all night."

I watched her bend over and take the buckle off Jumpy's belt and then I heard the sirens. I never seen so many people trying to get through one door at the same time. When Jerico took off, I stayed right behind him because Jumpy was coming back to life and he was mad as hell. By the time I made it out to the parking lot the cars and trucks were all headed out the same hole, try-ing to hit the highway before the do-right boys arrived. It was a regular demolition derby with horns a-honking, cowboys cussing, fenders bending and tires a-smoking. I looked over at my old beater just in time to see some drunk take out her front door with the winch on his pickup. And then Jack Sprat came along and kicked out the headlights. That's when I spotted ole Hank standing next to a shiny red Ford truck that was sporting a couple of fresh whiskey bumps.

"Hey Hank!" I hollered. "How come you're still here?"

"I been waiting on you. I was starting to worry about you and that leg of yours. You okay?"

"Oh yeah. I'll make it," I said as I watched the last gal in the place hop into her GTO and speed out of the lot. "But there goes my last chance for a soft heart and a warm bed."

"I been meaning to ask you if you need a place to lay up for awhile. You're welcome to stay with me as long as you want. Or at least till my ole lady comes home. She's over in Arkansas visiting with her sister. No telling when she'll be back. Hell, I think you and me could have some fun if we just put our minds to it."

"I'll sure enough take you up on that, Hank. But right now I think we might have to defect."

"Uh oh!" he said when he saw the sheriff heading in our direction. "Do you think we can get to Mexico before dawn?"

"Hell, yes. Where's your rig?"

He pointed to the red truck I was leaning on.

"She ain't as purty as she was when I got here tonight, but I'm sure she'll get us there."

"Well, what are we waiting for, pard?"

Clyde's Arc

A few years back I heard about something called the Darwin Award. Now, I seriously doubt that I'll ever be nominated for any of the good awards like an Oscar or a Tony. And for obvious reasons, I don't stand a chance of winning the Nobel Peace Prize, either. But that don't stop me from trying to get the recognition I think I deserve. If I could just get somebody's attention — somebody important like Mr. Pulitzer, or maybe that feller with the big black hat and the guitar — I might could make a name for myself. Do you know? They wouldn't even send me an application for the Country Music Awards when I called up there. I disguised my voice and everything, but the lady that answered the phone said: "Dan Burnett, is that you again?" And I answered: "No. But I'm one of his thousands of fans."

Maybe I been aiming too high. Maybe I ought to set my sights on that Darwin Award. I think I got about as good a chance of winning that one as anybody else. The last Darwin went to a guy who croaked when a Coke machine toppled over and mashed him. He was trying to get a free pop out of it. The worst part was, he had five dollars worth of change in his pocket when he died.

One thing's for sure. I been practicing for that award most all of my life. Being a cowboy, it sort of comes with the territory. And as for being a bull rider . . . well, that probably is about the closest a man could ever come to committing accidental suicide. In fact, it was after one of them near death experiences when I ran into Clyde Peck. I believe it was June of 67, right after my ride on ole Brown Bomber. That bull had stuck a horn through my cheek and loosened four or five teeth. I was so busted up, I had to go home to heal my wounds.

That was the worst part of rodeoing. I just hated to be laid up. But it was a good time to build up my poke. Nothing like having a little extra spending money for when I got back on the road. In fact, that's how come I happened to be talking to ole Clyde. I'd been breaking a few colts, doing a little horse trading, and hoping the boys over to the Double-R feed lot might have some horses I could trade my colts for. Clyde was the head cowboy at the Double-R, which meant he was responsible for general maintenance, and sometimes when the horseshoer couldn't get out there soon enough, he did that job, too. Generally there was about twenty thousand cattle feeding there, and it took ten or twelve cowboys to check all the pens for sick animals. It was a good way to put a nice handle on a horse in a fairly short time.

☆　☆　☆

It was dinnertime when I pulled up to the feed lot, so I went straight to the tack room where the cowboys were eating. You got to be tough to be a cowboy, even to scarf down your groceries. It was hot in there, and with all them cattle milling around the pens, the smell didn't exactly improve a feller's appetite. I was glad I had stopped in town at the diner.

Sure was easy to spot the single boys. The married ones had sandwiches but the unattached boys would eat just about anything that came in a can. One was wearing out a bottle of hot sauce trying to add some flavor to his Vienna Sausages, and another ole boy was poking around in a can of Pork-n-Beans with his pocket knife. He'd cut the top off and was using the blade for a fork. Now, I'd been on enough ranches and feed lots in my life, and I'll just bet he used the same knife to clean his horse's hooves that morning. Cowboys are known for keeping things simple. One real old feller had a tin spoon with a hole in the handle and baling wire strung through it. I figured he had probably learned a lesson or two from eating beans off a knife blade. When he got done eating, he wiped it off on his chaps and hung it up on a nail so he could find it the next day.

Clyde had already finished eating. He was stooped over behind a sorrel Quarter Horse, checking out its leg. I knew it was him because I recognized them boots of his.

"Hey Clyde. When are you going to get some new boots?"

Clyde was about fifty, tall, skinny, and a little bent here and there — a typical old cowboy except for one thing. He was shiny as a chrome bumper. Clyde had discovered duct tape. He used it to mend the seat covers in his pickup, to paste his Ace Reid calendar to the tack room wall, to patch his britches, and of course, to hold his old boots together. Even the other boys gave him a hard time about his silver lining.

"Hey Clyde," the one with the sausages hollered. "What you gonna do when they run out of duct tape at the hardware store?"

"Sounds like the boys are worried about you, Clyde," I said.

He finally recognized me.

"What are you doing out here you old horse thief?"

That's a cowboy's way of saying: What brings you to my office, you old embezzler you?

"I'm looking to see if any of these colts you're training is worth slipping in here for. After midnight, I mean. Got any I could sneak out the back gate with?"

"I'll save you the trouble, Hoss. I'll give you this one. He's bad footed."

I took a closer look.

"I don't know, Clyde. Looks like to me he needs to go shopping with you to the Boot Barn."

"Huh?"

"Any more duct tape on them boots and you could use them for reflectors on your stock trailer."

The other cowboys went to hee-hawing and slapping their chaps, which didn't improve Clyde's mood any.

"I wish all of you would get the hell out of here and leave me alone. I ain't spending no money on boots till the price comes down. Fifty dollars for a pair of boots is highway robbery. And even if I was willing to pay that much, I wouldn't buy nothing down at the Boot Barn. Not as long as they got that long-haired brat working there."

"Oh hell, Clyde," the old-timer spoke up. "That's Kenny Wallace's kid. He won't be there much longer. He's joining the Marines come fall."

"I don't give a damn if he joins Sweet Adelines. I ain't going back there and I ain't buying no boots. Hell, I just got these here broke in good."

Clyde was one the best men I ever saw breaking colts or riding bucking horses. I never seen that character even come close to getting bucked off. It was like he had glue on the seat of his pants. I seen him sit a horse that was turning inside out and he'd be carrying on

180

a conversation with someone sitting on the fence at the same time. Yessir, that ole boy could ride any horse alive. But Clyde had one little drawback. Once he got an idea in his head, the only way to get him to change his mind was to slap him upside the head with a hammer. And even if you did that, you'd risk ruining a good hammer, and chances are, Clyde wouldn't be impressed one bit.

Clyde told the boys to eat up and get back to work. As soon as they were out of sight, he turned to me for some advice, which took me by surprise.

"Hoss, I want you to take a look at this horse's foot." He ran his hand down the colt's hind leg, pulled it up and poked around the bottom of his hoof. "I think he's got a bruised frog. Stepped on a rock, I imagine. I sure hate to lose the training I already put on him but I guess I'm gonna hafta turn him out to heal. Unless you got any ideas."

"You tried a bar shoe? That might protect the bruise enough so you can keep riding him."

His eyes lit up.

"Say, that's a good idea. We got a welder right over there."

He dug around until he found an old horseshoe. He took it to the anvil, beat one side of it out straight, and then went and picked up the horse's sore foot again.

"That look about right, Hoss?"

I knew it wouldn't do no good to tell him it wasn't. Besides, he seemed to know what he was doing, and I figured I might learn something new if I just watched him.

Clyde lined up the straight part of the old shoe with the heel of the one that was on the horse. He made a mark in the rust with his thumbnail, grabbed a hacksaw and proceeded to cut it down to size. Then he pointed to the welder and put on his helmet.

"Plug that sucker in, will ya?"

Things was starting to get interesting. I went over to the welder, plugged it in and flipped the switch. Meanwhile, Clyde had found a couple of rods and stuck them in his hip pocket. By this time the horse was starting to take a keen interest in all the goings on, too. I figured he probably was a-wondering what that crazy old man was up to, and when Clyde went to stringing that ground lead over to him, I was a little curious myself.

"Clyde, just what are you planning to do with that thing?"

He looked at me like I had just asked the dumbest question in the book.

"I'm fixing to weld a bar on that shoe. Remember? You ought to. It was your idea, wasn't it?"

"Yeah, I guess it was. But you got to pull that old shoe off before you weld the bar to it."

"Now why in the hell would I pull a shoe I just nailed on last week? It won't take but a minute to weld it on, then I'll be done."

I just shook my head.

"Don't look at me like that," he frowned. "I got a lot to do around this place besides shoeing horses, you know. I can't see no sense making all that extra work."

"Clyde, you ain't the sharpest tool in the shed, are you?"

"Well, I ain't never been one to waste time, and except for you, there ain't nobody around here ever accused me of being a complete fool, either. So, if you ain't gonna help me, why don't you just get back in your truck and go for a ride."

That might have been the best thing for me to do, but if Clyde was dead set on causing a wreck, I sure enough didn't want to miss it.

"What the hell do you think that colt's going to do when you make an arc and all that electricity runs through him, Clyde?"

182

"Just shut up, Hoss."

"I'll bet you money and give odds he's going to kick your fool head off."

Clyde clenched his teeth and said, "I know what I'm doing, Hoss. Don't you think I ever welded before?"

"Yeah, but have you ever tried to weld something that was alive? I'm telling you, this little plan of yours ain't going to work."

No way was that ole boy backing down. He put his hands on his hips and screwed up his face so bad I thought he was trying to scare me off.

"Hoss, I'll just bet you a case of beer I'll be done in five minutes."

"You know how much I like beer, Clyde. Double or nothing."

"You're on!"

"Hold on just a minute," I said when I saw him reach for a rod. "Them is awful big stakes. Let me go round up some witnesses."

"Go ahead! Do whatever you want."

Ordinarily I wouldn't need a witness. As far as I knew, Clyde always paid up on a bet. But it's a might dull around a feed lot the biggest share of the time, and I just knew them cowboys would appreciate a good laugh.

"Hey boys," I hollered over the fence. "Clyde's going to give us a welding lesson this afternoon. Come on! I don't think you don't want to miss this."

Clyde was famous for his stubborn streak, and most of the boys were used to his dumb-ass stunts, but it was dang sure obvious that this one was going to get him in a world of hurt. They went to snickering and a-muttering to theirselves, and all agreed it was the stupidest thing any of them had heard of. Well, all except the Vienna Weenie kid who thought it just might work. He was a lot like Clyde. In fact, both of them was good candidates for the Darwin Award.

"Okay Clyde," I said. "Go ahead and show us how smart you are. I'm sure we got enough men here for pallbearers."

The colt was the only one that didn't know what was going on, but he suspected something was wrong when Clyde came at him with that helmet on. He was kind of interested in the audience, too. He started dancing a bit and them ole brown eyes was just a-rolling around in his head, trying to watch them cowboys and keep Clyde in sight at the same time.

"Hey, you lazy bums!" Clyde hollered as he hooked the ground lead to the shoe. "One of you get over here and help me with this horse."

No one moved.

"It's your show," I said. "Ain't nobody gonna get involved in this circus."

He give us a dirty look and mumbled, "Fine! I'll do it myself."

Clyde pulled down his helmet and touched the rod to the bar he was holding on the back of the shoe. That colt jumped straight up, and when he came down he was squalling and a-bucking like I ain't never seen. Clyde's hood went sailing, the horse stomped on his foot, and before he could get out of the way, the colt rared up again and kicked him square in the butt.

"Ow! Ow! Ow!" Clyde groaned as he slid in a heap in the corner of the stall.

He sure enough was a pitiful sight, all curled up in a little ball and moaning like he might be carried off to heaven any minute. Of course, we knew he wasn't too bad off, but we huddled around him just in case the colt had a mind to do some more damage.

It's times like this that I always like to console a feller by giving him some good advice. And by the looks of Clyde at that moment, he sure enough needed some

184

advice from someone. I squatted down beside him and spoke real loud so he could hear good.

"Clyde, if you was considering a change of careers, I wouldn't give up cowboying to be a welder just yet. And by the way, I was thinking . . ."

"You got five seconds, Hoss!" He pulled himself up off the floor and started after his torch. "I'm warning you, boy. If you don't get your skinny tail out of here, I'm gonna weld the fillings in your teeth together."

Well, my mouth was still tore up from the Brown Bomber's attack on me, and I really was not in the mood for any more dental work. I thought for a minute I might try and talk Clyde out of another welding lesson, but he was too worked up. Come to think of it, I never seen him that mad. There was fire in that ole man's eyes.

I stepped out of his way real quick like, unplugged the welder, and hooked it on out of there just as fast as I could. In fact, I left too fast I plum forgot about our little wager. Damn that was dumb of me!

Like I said, if I keep trying, I just might win that Darwin Award someday. Providing old Clyde doesn't beat me to it.

Live Wire

One summer day I was passing through Tucumcari on my way to Albuquerque when I decided to stop there at Orville's place. It was a hot, dusty day and I was hoping he would have a cold beer in his refrigerator.

I walked up to the door and knocked.

Nobody answered.

I looked through the window and saw that he wasn't there.

When I spotted his pickup parked on the back side of the barn, I figured he had to be around the place somewhere, so I went to looking. It didn't take long. He was out near the pens, squatted down on them skinny little bowed legs of his, and there was two license plates lying on the ground next to him. He was working up a sweat trying to get an old plate off the back bumper of his horse trailer.

In typical Orville fashion, he was a-cussing and a-mumbling to himself, so he didn't hear me coming up behind him.

I tiptoed up and said in a low, gruff voice: "Hey son! What do you think you're doing?"

Orville tossed his tools under the trailer and hopped to attention.

"Nothing, Sheriff."

When he saw it was me his eyes got big as tractor tires. He squinted at me and spit.

"You son-of-a-bitch. You scared me to death."

186

"Orville, if I was you, I wouldn't be sneaking around in daylight switching license plates. If you're not careful, you could end up making new ones in the pen down in Santa Fe someday. What you gonna do anyway? Steal some cattle?"

He scowled and then he kicked dirt at me.

"Maybe you're like them rich ole boys up north," I continued. "You know the type I mean. The ones that got started in the cattle business with a full moon and a big loop."

"I ain't never stole a cow in my life!"

I had only been there a minute and already I had him riled up.

"Damn, Orville, I sure didn't think times was that bad. If you're set on being a cattle rustler, I guess I'll have to start making some plans to come visit you after they capture you. I suppose you'll be wanting me to bring you cigarettes and all."

Orville scrunched his face up and grit his teeth. Even if I was intending to, I wouldn't do it around here. The old-timers around this country would shoot a man if they caught him stealing a cow. Anyway, if you'll shut up your jabbering, I'll tell you just what my idee is."

"So, what's your *idee*, Orville?" I laughed.

"Damn you, Hoss. You sure know how to get a man stirred up. What are you doing here anyway?"

"I'm just passing through. Now, tell me what your idea is."

"I'm going to the sale and pick up some sick cattle. Cheap." He had simmered down some. "I'm gonna doctor them, feed them good, and then I'll sell them back. The problem is my plates is outdated, and there's a new cop in town. That punk's going and giving everybody a ticket if their plates is expired."

"You're kidding me."

"No, I ain't. It's the truth. Ain't that something? Nobody around here has ever put plates on their trailers.

They're lucky if they can afford to put them on their trucks. That green kid gets a tin star and now he wants to show the world he's a big shot."

Orville bent over and looked under the trailer.

"Help me get them tools, Hoss."

"Where'd you get the plates, Orville? I don't know if I ought to be participating in this here operation. I don't usually do things that's against the law."

"You lying son of a . . . I got these here off a trailer down at the wrecking yard."

Well, that didn't sound too dangerous, so I rounded up Orville's tools and we switched the plates lickety-split.

"How about a cup a coffee, Hoss?"

"Well, I guess so. A cold beer would be better, but if coffee is all you got . . ."

"Good. Come on in and I'll fix you one. It's been awhile. You know something? I was afraid you might still be mad after that stunt I pulled in Mineral Wells."

"Naw."

"Good. Because I didn't know that airbase had grown over with brush. I was real surprised to see them big ole thorn trees with stickers four inches long. That stuff tore you up pretty bad. I thought we'd be crow bait the first day. Sure am glad you don't hold grudges. You don't, do you, Hoss?"

"Naw."

"Man! I thought ole Bubba was gonna kill you when we tried to rope him. You know that bull totaled two jeeps and run off a whole platoon of MP's before me and you got there."

"Yeah, I knew that. I wasn't too happy about the situation. But hell, we was broke at the time."

"I'm sorry we didn't get paid as much money as we thought we would. And I'm sorry ole Bubba gave you such a fit."

"So am I. But, to tell the truth, Orville, Bubba didn't scare me half as bad as that ex-galfriend you neglected to tell me about."

"I know I should have told you. Guess I just forgot. You sure you ain't mad about it, Hoss?"

"Orville, I told you, I ain't mad! But if you keep up this interrogation, I'm gonna get damn mad."

"Guess that means you ain't still sore about . . ."

"Orville!"

"Okay. Okay. I just wanted to make sure. I heard some stories about you getting even with ole boys that . . . "

"Don't pay no attention to them idiots. I thought you was gonna give me a cup of coffee."

"Okay. Come on in the house."

Now, Orville's and my idea of a house ain't exactly the same. That old shack he called home looked like the place them Tennessee hillbillies left behind when they moved out to Beverly Hills. I swear there was gaps in the walls you could throw a cat through.

I walked over to the kitchen table, which was really a sheet of plywood on a pair of sawhorses, and pulled up a chair. When I sat down, the back leg went plum through the floor. Most of the boards were rotten and there was one big gap under the kitchen sink where the pipe drained onto the ground outside. I was just gonna mention it to Orville when I spotted something fuzzy squeezing through the planks. It was a cat. That animal had to be the ugliest feline I'd ever seen. He was gray striped, sort of long haired, sort of short haired — depending on which part of him you was looking at — and his ears didn't match. One looked okay, but the other one was all frayed and stuck out in three different directions. His tail was crooked and his ole head was a mass of scars. There was a hollow on one side where his left eye was missing, and I guessed his jaw had been broke

189

once or twice because it had healed funny so his two bottom teeth stuck out sideways.

"Damn, Orville," I said as I watched that pitiful thing limping across the room. "Where'd you find this god-awful looking beast?"

"I didn't. He found me. Just showed up one day and moved in. Sure glad he's not a black cat. You know black cats are bad luck. My uncle took in a black cat once. The next day all his cattle died. Then his tractor broke and his house got haunted."

Orville was superstitious. We never could get him to go out dancing on Halloween. Even if they was giving away free booze.

"So, what's his name?"

"That's ole Good Eye." Orville bent down and patted the cat's head and that one eye shone yellow as a pumpkin. "Yep. That's the first thing I thought of when I saw him."

"Imagine that!"

Orville always did like to keep things simple. And he always had a soft spot for cats. He wasn't much on dogs, but he loved felines. I guessed Good Eye there reminded him of all the women that purred first and wanted to scratch his eyes out later.

"Hell of a mouser, too." Orville picked up the cat and hugged him. "Ain't you, ole buddy?"

That thing looked real comfortable there on Orville's lap, just a-purring and a-drooling.

"Orville! That stupid cat is slobbering all over you."

"He can't help it. I think it's because his mouth is all bent out of shape."

Orville put Good Eye in his chair while he went to the stove to get our coffee. He brought two cups and two saucers to the table and poured.

"A saucer? Who was you expecting? The Queen of England?"

"I always get a saucer out for Good Eye. Thought I'd just get you one, too." He walked over to the refrigerator and took out a pint jar. "You want cream?"

"Naw. Just black."

"Well, Good Eye likes cream."

Orville sat down and poured a little cream in the saucer next to his coffee cup, then he picked up Good Eye and held the saucer out so he could get a drink. That cat started lapping and a-purring like a new tractor. He looked so contented, I decided to reach over and pet him.

"Hold it!" Orville hollered as the cat jumped to the floor. "Good Eye don't like nobody touching him but me. He'd as soon bite you as look at you. I think he's part Chihuahua. Watch your ankles, Hoss."

I took his advice and kept my eyes on the cat as he wandered around the shack.

"You know, Orville, a cow could walk through those walls. I'll bet you got snakes in here, too."

"Nope. Good Eye keeps them out. You ought to see him. The other morning I heard him making that funny yowl like when he catches a mouse. He yowled for a good five minutes. Well, you know how I like to sleep in. So, when I didn't jump right out of the sack, he jumped up on the bed with a dead rattler in his mouth. How about that?"

"Sorry I missed that."

"Hell, he might do it again tomorrow. Can't never tell. By the way, you need a place to stay tonight?"

"I'm not sure if I'm desperate enough to spend the night here or not."

"Suit yourself."

We finished our coffee and Good Eye finished lapping up his milk.

"You want to help me feed?" Orville said real cheerful like helping him feed was fun.

"Sure."

191

Good Eye followed us out to the corrals and disappeared. I was grateful for that. It was hard enough keeping an eye on Orville and watch that damn cat, too. When we got to the barn Orville unplugged the fence charger and I held the wire down so he could step over it. I didn't feel like working too hard, so I let him do the heavy lifting. He threw a few flakes of hay to the scrawny cattle in the pen and then we headed back to the barn to plug the charger back in.

"I see you already picked up some of them sick cattle. I don't know why you waste electricity on them, Orville. There ain't a one of them healthy enough to walk away from this place."

"They're gonna be healthy in a day or two. I gave them penicillin shots and I been feeding them real regular. Can't afford to lose too many of them. It costs me some to doctor them up, you know. But I'll make a few bucks off of this bunch."

"Sounds like you're making a living, Orville."

"Just. Ain't no cowboy gonna get rich doing what we do. We found that out down there in Mineral Wells. Huh, Hoss?"

"Sure enough, Orville."

I gritted my teeth. Damn, I didn't need to be reminded again about that wreck in Texas.

By the time we got back to the house it was getting dark and I was hungry.

"You want to have supper with me and Good Eye."

"I don't know." I was used to Orville being superstitious and all, but I had never known him to read my mind before. "Are you fixing Little Friskies tonight?"

He punched me in the arm and Good Eye growled.

"Don't be stupid. Good Eye likes to eat Spaghetti-O's. Except on Wednesdays."

"Well, okay, I guess. As long as you're doing the cooking."

192

Orville started warming up the noodles but the cat had his eye on a different menu. That mouse sprinted across the room and ole Good Eye went to fixing his own supper.

"I swear, Orville, your damn cat is butt ugly! That mouse took one look at him and fell over dead."

"Be careful what you say," Orville chuckled. "I can't tell if he likes you yet or not."

"I'm going to sleep with your gun if I stay here tonight."

"Aw, come on, Hoss. He ain't that bad. He don't take up a lot of room, and he pays his own way. That's important when you're running a shoestring outfit like mine."

The next morning Orville cooked us fried eggs and ham for breakfast. We had our eggs sunnyside up, but ole Good Eye had to have his scrambled.

"You sure do pamper that cat, Orville."

"Hoss, finish your coffee, and don't be worrying yourself about my cat. I'm gonna run out and feed the stock."

I finished up my coffee about the same time Good Eye was cleaning up his eggs. He looked up at me with that big yellow eye and for a minute I thought I had inherited Orville's mind-reading powers. That cat was fixing to attack and I was his target. I hadn't got but an hour's sleep on account of Good Eye. He had spent the entire night running in and out of the cracks in the walls, and every time I got up to see what was going on, all I could see was that big ole eyeball glowing in the dark. Besides that, when I did doze off now and then, I kept on dreaming about Mineral Wells and how I was going to pay Orville back. Now was my chance.

Orville had stopped at the barn to unplug the charger. I waited for him to leave, then I snuck in and hid. Just as he reached for the fence, I plugged the charger back in. That ole boy went straight up in the air and came down straddling that hot wire. He let out a yowl and went to jumping and a-kicking like he was riding the buckingest bronc that ever lived. Before he got loose, I unplugged the charger and ran back to the house.

I was watching through the window when Orville went into the barn to check out the charger. When he came back out, he was shaking his head like he had just observed one of the world's greatest mysteries. He stared at the fence, then peeked around the barn to see if anybody was there. After a minute or two, he started back for the house, rubbing his butt and looking like he was lost. When he walked in the kitchen door, I was sitting there at the table with my coffee cup like I hadn't moved. Damn it was hard not to laugh. His clothes were all cock-eyed, his hat was on backwards, and he looked so confused that even his cat hissed at him.

"What are you looking at, you stupid cat?" said Orville as Good Eye ran between his legs and slinked under the bed.

"What's wrong, Orville?" I said real innocent like.

He muttered something I couldn't make out and poured himself some coffee.

"Damn, Orville. You been living out here so long, you forgot how to dress yourself?"

"The hell I have." He glared at me. "It's that damn fence charger. There's something wrong with it. I know I unplugged it before I went near the fence. Shit! I might near got electrocuted. I didn't think I was ever going to get loose from that wire. I'll be lucky if I can have kids now."

"That might be a blessing. They'd probably all look like ole Good Eye anyway."

"Smart ass!" He poured me another cup of coffee. "I'd have you take a look at that charger, but you don't even know how to operate an electric shaver."

I ignored the insult because it was true. I am no electrician and I was not going to learn to be one on Orville's watch. Besides, I was just starting to have fun.

"You know, Orville, I heard some old-timers talking one day. They said that sometimes them chargers take on a life of their own. There was an ole boy down in El Paso once that swore his talked to him."

Orville stared at me a minute, then he said: "That's bullshit. Ain't no fence charger can talk."

"Really? You ever been under them big power lines and heard them humming?"

Orville had that look that he gets when he's trying to think. After awhile his face lit up like a candle and he said: "Everybody's heard that. But humming ain't the same as talking."

"Exactly. But a charger has a pulse. If you listen real close, it sounds just like a heartbeat."

Orville gave me a suspicious look.

"Well, don't it?"

No doubt, Orville's brain was working overtime.

"If something's got a heartbeat," I continued, "It's alive ain't it?"

Orville was really confused.

"That feller from El Paso said his charger used to give him secret information, like where to find gold and stuff like that. I'd just hate to think that your charger had a tip about a horse race or something and you missed it. I think you might have one of them spirit-possessed chargers."

Now, Orville never was hasty, but he was curious. And he never passed up a chance to make a dollar.

"Whoever heard of electrical spirits?"

I got the feeling he was testing me. Orville knew me pretty well, and I thought he might go to reading my mind again. So, I decided to change my strategy.

"Well, Orville, if you don't want to listen to what that charger has got to say, maybe I'll mosey on out there and listen myself."

195

Now, the only thing that scared Orville more than ghosts was thinking somebody might beat him to a financial opportunity.

"I guess it couldn't hurt to take a listen," he said like he still wasn't too sure of himself. "But, I want you to come with me."

So, off we went to the barn. When we stood next to the charger we could hear it pulsating. Orville bent down close and concentrated hard. That bow-legged fart sure was good watching.

"See there, Orville," I chuckled to keep from laughing out loud. "Don't that sound like a heartbeat?"

"Damn Hoss, you're right! But I can't make out no words."

"That's 'cause the charger is the heart. It ain't your heart that talks when you go to say something. Is it?"

"No, smart ass. I know that."

At last I was making a connection.

"You got to go outside and listen to the wire to make it out clear."

Orville grinned like he had figured it all out by himself. He went outside to the wire and I sat on a bale wondering just what kind of racing tips he was going to get from his haunted hot line. He squatted down close to listen, and when he didn't hear anything he laid down flat under the wire. He wiggled and squirmed on the ground for a good ten minutes before he gave up.

"I don't hear a doggone thing, Hoss. You sure we done everything right?"

"Maybe it doesn't know you're there. After all, a fence don't have any eyes. Maybe you should say something to it."

"I ain't stupid you know. What would people think if they was to see me talking to an electric fence?"

"Hell, Orville. What people are you talking about? There ain't nobody here except me and Good Eye. And

196

you done scared him off already. Besides, if you make a fortune at the track, people will probably pay you big money to talk to their fences."

"Okay. But if you tell anybody, I'll kill you."

"Orville, I'm hurt you'd even think such a thing."

"I'll bet you are."

Orville squatted down again and spoke almost in a whisper. "Hey fence spirit. It's me. Orville. You got anything you want to tell me?"

Lucky for me, the wind had kicked up a good bit by then and that made it real easy for me to disguise my voice. I cupped my hands around my mouth and spoke real low: "Hello, Orville."

Orville sprang to his feet.

"Did you hear that?"

"Hear what?" I said with a surprised look. "It must be the wind."

Orville looked up at the sky and then back at the fence.

"I don't think so. I heard 'hello Orville'." He sat down close to the fence again. "Are you a spirit?"

"Yes-sss," I said with my hand over my mouth to muffle the sound.

"Can you tell me a secret way to make money on cattle?"

"Buy loooow. Sell hiiiigh."

Orville got plum excited. He started jumping up and down so much I thought for sure his hat would come off.

"It talked to me, Hoss. It really talked. It even told me how to make money selling cattle."

"What did it say?"

"I ain't telling you. You'd just say it was the wind. But it wasn't. It was a secret message just for me. Go and find your own fence spirit."

Boy, was it hard not to bust out laughing.

"Is that all it had to say?"

"I don't know." Orville bent down and asked: "Have you got any more messages for me?"

"Touch me," whispered the fence.

"No way!" Orville yelled as he jumped back from the fence. "The last time I touched you, I damn near got fried."

"Unplug first," the fence advised him.

Orville started to walk toward the charger but the fence spoke again. "No. You stay."

Orville stood there a minute thinking, which was always a dangerous activity for him.

"Hoss, I think you should go unplug this thing. I think it wants to talk to me in private."

"All right," I said.

I could hardly wait to get back inside the barn and out of Orville's sight. I squatted in a corner and laughed till I cried.

After I got myself together, I turned the fence off and hollered at Orville: "Okay. She's unplugged."

Orville was still a little snakey. He reached out with his fingertips and slapped the wire real quick. He repeated that a couple of times, then he grabbed it with one hand and pulled it up close to his ear. When he didn't hear anything, he grabbed it with both hands and held it up to his other ear.

"What's it saying?" I asked.

"I can't hear a thing now."

"Oh, I get it. You just don't want to tell me. Ain't that right?"

When he gave me that empty stare like he was starting to think again, I plugged the charger back in.

"I reeeeeeeeally . . ."

He squealed like a stuck hog when the juice hit that wire. His feet shot out behind him, his hair stood straight up, and if there had been a couple more volts coming out of that charger, I'm sure he would have lit up like a Christmas tree.

When I figured he'd had about enough of them inspirational messages, I unplugged the charger real quick and ran up to him and sat him down on a bale. His eyeballs were still spinning.

"What was your special message, Orville? It must be exciting the way you jumped. Aw, come on. You can tell me, can't you?"

"Hell no! It didn't tell me anything. The damn thing short-circuited. It might near welded my teeth together." He rubbed his frizzled hair. "I think it's gone and fried my brain."

"Orville, you're brain was fried a long time ago."

Orville studied me a minute, then he got that real suspicious look in his eye again.

"Hoss, did you turn that damn thing back on?"

"Of course not!"

I tried to look offended.

"Where you going?" I asked when Orville started for the barn.

"You told me these things got a life of their own. Well, I'm fixing to end the life of one fence spirit."

Before I could stop him, Orville grabbed an old piece of pipe and beat the charger to death. When he gave it a kick for good measure, I couldn't hold it any longer. I started laughing like a hysterical woman. I just couldn't help it.

It took him awhile, but Orville finally realized that he'd been had.

"Damn you, Hoss. I thought you said you wasn't mad at me. You been lying to me since you got here."

"Orville, you know better than that," I grinned. "A cowboy never lies."

ORDER FORM

Please send the following:

_____ copy(s) of *A Cowboy Never Lies* at $12.95 each.

_____ set(s) of *Favorite Stories from A Cowboy Never Lies* on audio tape at $12.95 each.

_____ copy(s) of *A Cowboy Never Lies 2* at $12.95 each.

Shipping & Handling. Please add $3.00 for the first book or tape and $1.00 for each additional book or tape.

Sales Tax. Washington State residents must add 7.8% sales tax to each order.

Send order to:

NAME:_____

ADDRESS: _____

CITY:_____STATE:_____ ZIP:_____

PHONE:(_____)_____ FAX: (_____)_____

E-MAIL: _____

◇Check/money order (U.S. Funds) enclosed.

◇Charge my credit card:

VISA ACCT No. _____ EXP. DATE _____

M/C ACCT No. _____ EXP. DATE _____

SIGNATURE: _____

◇I do not wish to order at this time. Please send information about other New West Press Publications.

Copy or remove this page and mail to:

NEW WEST PRESS, PO BOX 32, HAMILTON, WA 98255

About the Author

According to Dan Burnett, there's only one difference between a storytelling rodeo cowboy and an author.

"Folks used to say I was plum crazy. Now they just say I'm eccentric."

Burnett's career as a working cowboy spanned a quarter century. It was, and still is, a tough way to make a living. Rodeo is even tougher. As a professional bronc and bull rider, Dan probably earned a lot more respect than money. And in the early days, the same could be said for his yarn spinning. But many of the faithful fans who followed him from town to town on the rodeo circuit — and from bar to bar after the show — still enjoy his hilarious escapades to this day.

After reading Dan's first book, long-time friend and rodeo buddy Jim Standifer said: "It always was hard to decide which was best — the watchin' or the listenin'. But seeing it in print sure does conjure up some good memories. There's a ton of laughs on every page."

Since the release of *A Cowboy Never Lies* in 1996, Burnett has been a regular guest on radio stations coast to coast. And several publications, including *The Western Horse,* have given his book excellent reviews. The encouragement has prompted Dan to continue personal performances around the country, and in response to requests from his fans, he also has recorded some of their favorite stories on audio tape. *(See previous page for ordering information.)*

Burnett, who grew up in New Mexico near the Texas border, currently lives in Washington State. When he's not telling stories, he shoes horses — a full-time job in the summer — and enjoys the companionship of his wife, two dogs and "the world's grouchiest cat."

Eccentric? Well, we'll let you be the judge of that. For those of you who have waited patiently for this latest collection of memorable tales, you'll be happy to know that Dan is spending every spare moment writing stories for his third book.

— *DIANE FREETHY, Editor*